TOD BROWNING'S
THE REVOLT OF THE DEAD

Gary D. Rhodes

Robert Guffey

Will Dodson

Nathaniel Bell

Jan Alan Henderson

Published by BearManor Media
1317 Edgewater Dr #110
Orlando FL 32804
www.bearmanormedia.com

Library of Congress Cataloguing-in-Publication Data
Rhodes, Gary D.
Tod Browning's *The Revolt of the Dead* / Gary D. Rhodes
p.cm.
ISBN 979-8-88771-003-7 (Hardback)
ISBN 979-8-88771-002-0 (Paperback)

1. The Revolt of the Dead.   2. Horror Film Scripts.   I. Rhodes, Gary D.   II. Scripts from the Crypt.   III. Title.
PN1997.T5335.R11 2022

CHASTAIN (props to
WILLIAM MORTENSEN)

A faux-movie poster created in 2022 by George Chastain for Tod Browning's unmade film
The Revolt of the Dead.

Table of Contents

Many of the illustrations in this book are from...

The John Antosiewicz Collection

The Perils of Hollywood Folklore

A Foreward by Jan Alan Henderson

Tod Browning when he was an actor at Biograph in 1913.

Remember that old saying, "When the legend becomes fact, print the legend."

Tod Browning was as much of a mystery as some of the films he is famous for. A deeply private individual, he has been almost impossible to chronicle. That is the process that generates folklore: tales of drinking, affairs with underage females, the perverse subjects of his films, and a rumored dash of sadism. These factors contribute to the mystique. Add to that the automobile accident of 1915 that killed one and desperately injured Browning and a fellow passenger. With no arrest and sparse information on the condition of the survivors, the environment was ripe for sordid rumors.

David J. Skal's 1993 book *The Monster Show* presents the reader with an unfocused diatribe about Browning's psyche and how it affected his art. Skal quoted Sigmund Freud's post–World War I essay "Das Unheimliche" ("The Uncanny"), leaning heavily on the castration complex as his argument for Browning's recurring themes of disembodied hands and heads, dismembered limbs and premature burial. He does concede that the public records of Browning's car accident were insufficient in detail and de-

scription of Browning's injuries to confirm (as he puts it) pelvic trauma. Without facts and proof, this is pure speculation; another brick in the wall of mythology.

Two years later, *Dark Carnival* by Skal and Elias Savada delved deeper into Browning's life and art. Interesting was Browning's disagreement with the Metro brass over the climax of what some would say was his most controversial film, *Freaks* (1932). According to Skal and Savada, the studio favored a more gruesome ending than Browning had planned. One hopes that Browning's psyche wasn't as damaged as has been speculated. He wanted a sad ending instead of the macabre ending the studio preferred. Maybe Browning had more empathy for the deformed and downtrodden than his unwritten psycho-diagnostic battery has indicated.

Freaks proved the final nail in Browning's directorial career coffin. He made a handful of films after *Freaks*, but this one picture caused more uproar and folklore than the 1915 car accident. Adding to the longevity firestorm was Dwain Esper's 1947 reissue of *Freaks* as *Forbidden Love*, playing often with other exploitation films (*Damaged Lives* [1933], *Reefer Madness* [1936], *The Wages of Sin* (1938). This late '40s reissue put *Freaks* in the sleaze cinema gutter. Other reissue titles that Esper put on *Freaks* were *Nature's Mistakes* and *The Monster Show*. Patrons expecting an erotic experience were sorely disappointed and fled theaters the same way as 1932 moviegoers.

Browning's next film for Metro was *Fast Workers* (1933), another financial disappointment. After a two-year dry spell, Browning's returned to work with an MGM remake of his own 1927 *London After Midnight*, a vehicle for Lon Chaney. The remake, *Mark of the Vampire* (1935) with Lionel Barrymore, did not set box offices on fire, but it was successful enough that Browning was employed on another MGM production, *The Devil-Doll* (1936). With Barrymore again in the starring role and the dynamic special effects, Browning turned in another acceptable film, basically earning about the same amount as *Mark of the Vampire*.

Browning had to wait a long three years for his next opportunity. In 1939, he was given his last directorial assignment, *Miracles for Sale*. A mystery with a few comedic elements and a magical premise, it bears many of the trademarks that made Browning famous.

In a phone conversation with me, Cortlandt Hull (the great-nephew of actor Henry Hull) described his great-uncle's participation in *Miracles for Sale*:

> Uncle Henry was working on another picture at the time he shot *Miracles for Sale*. He told me that it was a B-movie that was shot very quickly. Contrary to the credit listings, Uncle Henry played both Dave Duvallo and the Tauro character. Makeup artist Jack Dawn fashioned the prosthetic nose that Uncle Henry wore, but the real problem was the contact lenses. The lenses were hard and he could only wear them for half an hour at most, because of the pain. They greatly impaired his vision, and Browning took care to accommodate him by keeping his shots mostly stationary. Uncle Henry and Tod Browning worked well together, and it was an incident-free shoot.

Will people see beyond the folklore and appreciate Browning's work without prejudice? It took almost 30 years for serious film scholars to rediscover Browning's work.

In *Dark Carnival*, Samuel Marx is quoted on Browning's fall from grace at Metro, where Eddie Mannix was his sole supporter. Browning and Mannix spent Sundays together with the proviso that business matters were taboo topics in their social interaction. Browning hung around Mannix's office on weekdays, apparently getting no work, until the ax finally dropped. In 1944, his wife passed away. His last years were challenging, to say the least.

Actors Lionel Atwill, Colin Clive and George Zucco have all fallen victim to Hollywood folklore: Clive the tragic alcoholic, dead at 37; Atwill's blue movie antics put him at odds with the legal system; and poor Zucco, whose severe stroke generated wild tales of madness and Ed Wood auditions. All were chewed up in the folklore cheese grater. The same holds true for directors Alfred Hitchcock and James Whale. As much pain as this must have caused when they were alive, one thing is certain: The Hollywood folklore made them legends.

With *The Revolt of the Dead*, we have one more piece of the Tod Browning puzzle. It went unfilmed, so we can only speculate on what type of film this would have been. One can ponder what *The Unholy Three* (1925), *The Road to Mandalay* (1926), *The Unknown* (1927), *London After Midnight*, *Dracula* (1931) and *Freaks* would have been like if Tod Browning had not been in the director's chair.

Dracula has been labeled stagy and stiff by critics. Today we have the opportunity to view *Dracula* on Blu-ray and gain a whole new perspective on this timeless classic. It is a silent symphony of atmosphere, and Browning's direction perfectly frames Bela Lugosi's performance, adding an uncanny ambience that has yet to be rivaled, the eerie silence of the vampire. Browning's carefully paced direction allows the viewer to experience the terror in the dead of night. Browning captured Lugosi's nocturnal pantomime. Lugosi said a year later, when asked about the *Dracula* makeup, "It's not so much a makeup as it is an expression." Lugosi's Dracula

Tod Browning (left) on *Dracula*'s Lucy's Bedroom set with players Frances Dade and Helen Chandler.

prowls Dr. Seward's sanatorium like a black panther, with hypnotic orbs that paralyze all who encounter him, thanks to Charles D. Hall's atmospheric sets and Karl Freund's stylish cinematography.

These trademarks grace all of Browning's genre films. Like all things in culture, whether it be literature, music or cinema, nothing goes away. While great works are forgotten, they never vanish entirely. We can only hope that Tod Browning's work will be still be appreciated by future generations.

Browning was an actor, director and writer from 1915 to 1941, 26 years of creativity. He had a carnival background — as a living corpse, a black-faced comedian, and barker — so it's no wonder that he is viewed as an outré character, on the fringes of reality. If we move forward by coming from, we must preserve cinema history accurately. It seems folklore and mythology are unlikely to vanish any time soon.

There are many definitions of genius. One involves thousands of hours of work. If that is so, then Tod Browning qualifies. Legends begin life as mere mortals, but craft ensures that they attain immortality!

Introduction

by Gary D. Rhodes

> *People like to be shocked, mystified,*
> *and surprised, if it's done properly.*
> – Tod Browning

Tod Browning (1880-1962) remains enigmatic, even though it has been over eight decades since he directed his last movie. From silent to sound, from natural to supernatural, his horrors became our horrors, their images and stories illuminated eerily in the darkest reaches of our minds, our memories and our culture.

His adherents are many, ranging from Andrew Sarris and Ray Bradbury to Philip Glass and Nicolas Cage. His detractors, at least in the late twentieth and early twenty-first centuries, are legion, though their comments sometimes read less like scholars than plagiarists, less like thinkers than parrots, repeating the same criticisms (sometimes with the very same words) and mistakes as their predecessors. It is indeed unfortunate to hear even legitimate historians incorrectly state that, for example, George Melford's *Drácula* (1931) features more moving camera shots than Browning's *Dracula* (1931), when math as simple as could be managed by a fifth grader dispels that notion.

Browning deserves a biographer who actually enjoys his films, if only to counter the overly harsh opinions held by the likes of David J. Skal, who wrote *Dark Carnival: The Secret World of Tod Browning, Hollywood's Master of the Macabre* (1995), but who seems not to even agree with his book's title, at least insofar as any mastery is concerned. By contrast, novelist and scholar Robert Guffey — author of *Chameleo* (2015) and *Widow of the Amputation and Other Weird Crimes* (2021) — believes in the power of Browning's cinema. His chapter in this book provides appropriate context

and apotheosis for a filmmaker whose oeuvre will outlast all of his critics.

To be sure, this book is not a biography. It is instead an examination of Browning's narrative, thematic and visual concerns in relation to his script-to-screen process. What is inside the now-yellowing pages of script drafts and treatments, the characters and scenes that were too potent for studios and the Production Code? What did Browning see, in his imagination, that we haven't previously seen, because it never made it into a final cut, or because it was never even filmed? For the man behind such movies as *Dracula*, the questions are worthwhile, and the answers often surprising.

While Browning directed many films, more than a dozen of them deserving renewed focus, study and accolades, this book concentrates on four projects, the first three being *Freaks* (1932, in a chapter by Nathaniel Bell), *Mark of the Vampire* (1935, in a chapter by myself) and *The Devil-Doll* (1936, in a chapter by Will Dodson). All are important to his filmography. More specifically, the choices here were led by surviving archival materials and access to them. Script drafts for the trio, some probably unread for decades, are available at the Margaret Herrick Library of the Academy of Motion Picture Arts and Sciences in Beverly Hills.

The fourth project under review herein is *The Revolt of the Dead*. As with Browning's other films, the story underwent various evolutions, but it never made it to the screen. The trade press indicated that Browning would direct *The Revolt of the Dead* for MGM in late 1932. Like so many screenplays, it never made it past pre-production, it never twinkled in Tinseltown. But unmade films deserve attention for various reasons, including the light they shed on the artists who wrote them.

Browning (seated) on the set of *The Big City* (1928), now a lost film, with Lon Chaney and screenwriter Waldemar Young. Browning also collaborated with Young on *The Unholy Three, The Mystic, The Show, The Unknown, London After Midnight, West of Zanzibar, Where East Is East* and others. (Photo courtesy the Michael F. Blake Collection.)

Browning (with hat) consults with the Unholy Three — Lon Chaney, Harry Earles and Victor McLaglen — the stars of his 1925 same-name film. (Photo courtesy the Michael F. Blake Collection.)

Browning and Lon Chaney on the set of *The Road to Mandalay* (1926). (Photo courtesy the Michael F. Blake Collection.)

Given that *The Revolt of the Dead* does not exist as a film, we reproduce the entirety of its script in this volume, as well as treatment materials and notes, most from the personal collection of Tod Browning. Here is the opportunity to see Browning at work, behind the scenes, before any filming, as storyteller, screenwriter and collaborator on what is assuredly a "Script from the Crypt."

Browning once said, "You can shock the world, but you can't shock Hollywood." In most cases, he was correct, but it is possible, quite possible, that *The Revolt of the Dead* would have shocked the film capital in 1932 had it been produced.

Together with my friends Nathaniel Bell, Will Dodson and Robert Guffey, I bid you welcome to the shadowed screens of Tod Browning, who was indeed a master of the macabre.

"We Didn't Lie to You, Folks!": The Thin Line Between Deception and Foma in the Worlds of Tod Browning

by Robert Guffey

Of Mystics, Freaks and Miracles

Anyone interested in the history of the *fantastique* must contend with the spirit of Tod Browning. Not only was he the first American director brave enough to confront the supernatural in sound cinema without rationalizing it away — in the form of his 1931 adaptation of *Dracula*, his most famous work — but he also left behind a legacy of unique and original films, many of which are black jewels filled with scintillating and shocking surprises. If you only know Browning through *Dracula*, you can't really understand the true depth of his talent. It's difficult to think of a contemporary director who might be in any way comparable to Browning and his weird obsessions. The only American director I can think of, who might fit the bill, is David Lynch, who has created one dark masterpiece after another since his 1977 debut with *Eraserhead*. Time after time, Lynch has dug into the troubled inner lives of his tortured characters through means both mundane and phantasmagoric. That juxtaposition, of the real and the hyperreal, overlaps with the pioneering work of Tod Browning, master illusionist.

Browning was, to say the least, an extremely successful director in his day. Mainstream tastes ebb and flow, the pendulum swings from left to right and back again, and somehow over the years since his death in 1962, Browning's reputation has steadily diminished among film scholars and fans. The central reason appears to be the notion that his adaptation of *Dracula* is too stagebound and lackluster for modern audiences. This view appears to stem from a series of books written by film scholar David J. Skal, particularly *Hollywood Gothic* (1990), *The Monster Show* (1993) and *Dark Carnival* (1995), the latter a Browning biography. In these books, and on his *Dracula* DVD commentary, Skal has promulgated various misperceptions about Browning that seem to contradict each other. At various times, Skal has claimed that *Dracula* was **A)** badly directed by Tod Browning, resulting in a film too beholden to its stage origins, **B)** actually directed by its cinematographer Karl Freund, and/or **C)** not directed by anybody at all. It should be obvious that all three of these possibilities can't be true at the same time, and yet Skal often weaves all three scenarios together as if these alternative realities could easily co-exist in a single reality.

The idea that Browning was somehow incapable of directing *Dracula* flies in the face of the numerous films we know that Browning did direct. *Dracula* does not exist in a vacuum. Browning directed 62 films. Cineastes — scholars and fans alike — should track down at least some of these films before judging Browning's entire career based on a single project. Anyone interested in the history of the grotesque and arabesque, in either literature

Though *Dracula* is Browning's most famous movie and *Freaks* his most infamous, I contend that two of the ten films he made in collaboration with Lon Chaney are his masterpieces: *The Unknown* and *West of Zanzibar*. Unlike many movies made during the silent era, these particular films have emotional impact that has not diminished at all. Given the current state of the film industry, in which a movie that aspires to be anything more than a feel-good, lowest-common-denominator soporific is rarely produced, it boggles my mind that depressing films like *The Unknown* and *West of Zanzibar* were ever box office draws. I've often wondered what peculiar, mind-altering substance was introduced into illegal liquor of the 1920s to make Lon Chaney a movie star.

The modern perception of Chaney is that he was an actor who specialized in horror roles, but even a cursory glance at his résumé reveals that this was not the case at all. Apart from *The Phantom of the Opera* (1925), Chaney never starred in a film that could be strictly classified as "horror." No, Chaney's specialty was a starkly psychological form of Greek tragedy in which the protagonist often came to a terrible end through either a cruel twist of fate or his own hubris. Browning, too, was attracted to characters who were both physically and psychologically twisted. That these two men should collaborate on ten films was, perhaps, destined. But why hordes of average Americans should have been rabidly attracted to such dark films is beyond me. There's no modern equivalent to Chaney in today's world. There's no box office movie star whose specialty is making people thoroughly depressed. A Lon Chaney marathon of such films as *He Who Gets Slapped* (1924), *Mockery* (1927), *The Unknown* (1927), *Laugh, Clown, Laugh* (1928) and *West of Zanzibar* (1928) would instill in most modern audiences a sudden need for a steady Prozac prescription.

The Unknown and *West of Zanzibar* cast a haunting, hypnotic spell on those who saw them in theaters upon first release. In one of Ray

Tod Browning (July 12, 1880–October 6, 1962).

or film, has many treasures awaiting them in the works of Tod Browning.

With the extinction of Browning's *London After Midnight*, modern fans of the *fantastique* are left with a dozen Browning films. You should be intimately familiar with them because, whether you know it or not, Browning's films are part of the very DNA of the fantastique in world literature:

The Unholy Three (1925)
The Mystic (1925)
The Show (1927)
The Unknown (1927)
West of Zanzibar (1928)
Where East Is East (1929)
The Thirteenth Chair (1929)
Dracula (1931)
Freaks (1932)
Mark of the Vampire (1935)
The Devil-Doll (1936)
Miracles for Sale (1939)

On the *London After Midnight* set, Lon Chaney (right) learns some *Easy Lessons in Hypnosis* (alongside Tod Browning and teenage actress Marceline Day), and now he's ready to ...

... apply what's he learned, first to Browning alone ...

... and then to Browning *again*, this time with some help from co-star Conrad Nagel.

Browning and Lon Chaney during the making of *The Road to Mandalay.*

Bradbury's final interviews ("Ray Bradbury's Earliest Influences," *Monsters from the Vault* #30), he described for Terry Pace the impact of Browning and Chaney on his pre-pubescent imagination:

> There's … a dark and rather twisted film [Chaney] made with Tod Browning, *West of Zanzibar*, where Chaney plays a crippled carnival magician in the African jungle who has a trick coffin with a skeleton in it. When Chaney's magician needs to convince the natives that he has magical powers, he puts someone into that trick coffin. When the lid opens again, that person disappears and the skeleton appears in the coffin in his place. The magician element of that particular

Chaney character certainly shows up in the master of my own macabre carnival — the evil character of Mr. Dark in my supernatural novel *Something Wicked This Way Comes.*[1] But in the end, Chaney's performances weren't simply a matter of monsters, makeup and magic tricks. Even when his characters are menacing or morally misguided, his films are all very moving because those characters are all struggling somehow with the heartbreak of unrequited love. I think that's something that all of us — even small children — can understand and appreciate in Chaney's films after all these years. After all, love and acceptance are what we all want from the very beginning of our lives.

I hesitate to analyze *West of Zanzibar* too deeply for the benefit of those of you who have never seen this film. You should be allowed to discover this weird treasure with fresh eyes. Suffice it to say that both *The Unknown* and *West of Zanzibar* are the kinds of movies that novelist Kurt Vonnegut liked to call "mind-fucks," psychoshamanic shadow-shows that show no mercy to their audiences in a torturous, unrelenting manner that's quite out of step with modern filmmaking. How many films and TV shows have you seen in which the filmmakers lost their nerve and stepped back from the edge at the very last moment? How many films have you seen in which the only logical conclusion would be the death of the protagonist, and then abruptly everything is turned around because somebody in control of the funds decided that the audience could not be allowed to go home in an unhappy mood? Suddenly, a cure for cancer emerges from an angelic light, or the cavalry comes riding over the hill.

These unlikely possibilities did not exist in the benighted worlds of Tod Browning and Lon Chaney. If you were lining up to see a film starring Chaney, you were guaranteed an emotional wringer that was almost certain to make you feel discomfited and depressed. What 21st century movie studio would bankroll a performer whose whole brand was discomfiture and depression? This is something that *could not* happen these days, in which commercial art is only bankrolled as a numbing palliative for the sick at heart. During the Roaring Twenties of F. Scott Fitzgerald and *The Great Gatsby*, something dark and lonely — nailed down at the hollow center of the American spirit — was wriggling in its agonizing death throes at the edge of a psychological precipice from which there would never be any safe return. Nonetheless, audiences kept coming back for more. It's almost as if Chaney was a surrogate Christ figure whose specialty was absorbing all the free-floating pain that the average person was not allowed to express in those pre–Depression days in which not even alcohol was a legal escape for the terminally unhappy. You were compelled, by law, to be content with your lot in life and alcohol-free — or *else*. And if you didn't like it, go talk to your priest.

Or, go to the local movie house for a quarter and see a Tod Browning movie starring Lon Chaney, the Man of a Thousand Death Scenes. You were sure to say to yourself, when the lights went up, "At least I'm not as bad off as that poor fool." Let's face it, the latter route would probably be a far more effective way to deal with terminal depression in the 1920s. No confessional booth could beat the movie theater downtown. And no film other than those starring Chaney was guaranteed to give the viewer the vicarious thrill of watching someone more grotesque than you get beaten into the ground by an angry and unsympathetic God.

It's important to point out that the lands in which Browning traversed alone, without Chaney at his side, were no less dark. Both *The Mystic* (1925) and *The Show* (1927) can be seen, in retrospect, as dry runs for *Freaks*. But these works stand on their own, apart from their thematic similarities to Browning's most controversial film. *The Show*, in particular, showcases Browning's love for exploring the most shadowy areas of the human mind.

Browning's formative experiences working at sideshows and carnivals provided him with priceless background material for his most important projects: *The Unholy Three, The Mystic, The Show, The Unknown, Freaks* and *Miracles for Sale*. Browning understood the complex and seedy world of entertainment and illusion-making. He understood that there was both a positive and a negative side to these convincing illusions. In film after film, often with the help of screenwriter Waldemar Young, Browning explored the dichotomy between these two polar-opposite effects.

1. *The Unholy Three* (1925)

In *The Unholy Three,* a trio of carnival performers use the trickery they've picked up from a life spent in sideshows to pull off a brilliant con job. Echo the Ventriloquist (Chaney), Hercules the Strongman (Victor McLaglen) and Tweedledee the Dwarf (Harry Earles, who will later portray Hans in *Freaks*) form an "unholy" alliance to steal valuables from the rich. Echo pretends to be an elderly grandmother, Tweedledee a harmless infant and Hercules the infant's guardian. Rosie O'Grady (Mae Busch), Echo's pickpocket girlfriend, becomes a somewhat reluctant accomplice, pretending to be Tweedledee's mother.

Unholy Three director Tod Browning poses with Lon Chaney and his ventriloquist's dummy Nemo.

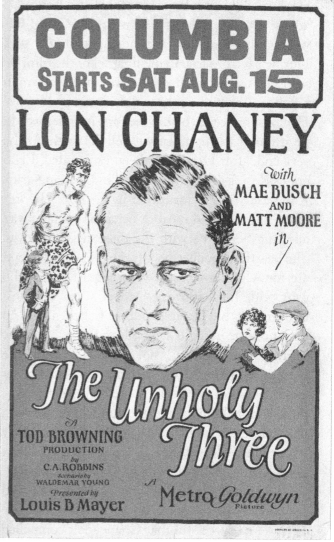

The four of them open a pet store which is nothing more than a cover for their thievery. While delivering pets to the homes of their well-to-do patrons, Echo and Tweedledee are able to case the joints, then return under the cover of darkness to relieve the unknowing customers of their valuables. Echo is adamant that no one should ever be killed during these robberies. He doesn't even want Hercules or Tweedledee to carry guns. Hector McDonald (Matt Moore) is hired to work in the pet store only so that the trio will have someone to frame if they find themselves in a jam with the law. Echo's intense jealousy over Rosie's growing intimacy with Hector prevents him from joining Hercules and Tweedledee on their latest robbery. Expectedly, the duo strays from Echo's orders: They take extreme measures during the break-in, murdering a man and harming a child. Now the police must investigate the robberies far more intensely than before.

Detective Regan (Matthew Betz) discovers that Mrs. O'Grady, the kindly old pet store owner, had been in the murdered man's house the previous day and saw the now-stolen rubies. The detective decides to interview Mrs. O'Grady, which convinces the trio to frame Hector. Rosie, now in love with Hector, tries to prevent this, to no avail.

We see in this plot the yin and yang of deception and *foma*,[2] i.e., positive and negative lies. The deception employed by the thieves leads to multiple murders. By the end of the film, at least three people have been killed and a child severely injured. But we also see the sideshow crooks using their talents at deception to try to right the wrongs they have committed. First, we see Rosie lie to Hector, using her acting skills to convince him she doesn't love him at all, that she's just been toying with him this entire time. She does this to save the man's life. Fueled by his intense love for Rosie, Echo also attempts to save Hector's life with the hope of salvaging his crumbling relationship with the girl. During Hector's trial in the final act of the film, we see Echo use his unique talent for ventriloquism in a futile attempt to create an illusion that will prove Hector's innocence before the jury. In other words, he attempts to use trickery to tell the truth. At the very end, after Hector has been exonerated, Echo erases Rosie's debt to him by pulling the same trick Rosie used on Hector earlier in the film: He pretends not to be in love with her, pushing her away, allowing her to be with the man she truly loves. The heartfelt goodbye he utters to Rosie at the end are funneled through his ventriloquist doll. Echo can't bring himself to use his true voice. Only his dummy can bid Rosie goodbye. Echo's name, no doubt a stage name, is symbolic of the fact that the ventriloquist's identity is not genuine; his entire life is an echo of an illusion crafted on one stage after another. As we saw in the courtroom, his first impulse is to tell the truth while performing through his doll; his default move is to tell the truth only while lying. Ultimately, Echo uses *foma*, a positive deception, to right the wrongs of his previous lies.

The Unholy Three was one of Browning and Chaney's most commercially successful collaborations — so successful that Chaney felt compelled to remake the film five years later as his first sound film, a project that would end up being his final bow, as the actor died of throat cancer only a month after the remake's release. One can see *The Unholy Three*'s influence in disparate artifacts of pop culture such as the enduring Chuck Jones cartoon "Baby Buggy Bunny" (1954), Ray Bradbury's "The Beggar on O'Connell's Bridge" (1961), in which an adult pretends to be an infant as a scheme to swindle people, and an endless slew of Hollywood "heist films" (beginning with Phil Karlson's *5 Against the House*, 1955) that generally involve a gang of clever tricksters who intend on hijacking money from the idle rich armed with little more than guts, brains and overly complicated ideas for the Ultimate Con Job.

2. *The Mystic* (1925)

In *The Mystic*, the dichotomy between positive and negative lies is pushed even further. In Hungary, a trio of gypsies, working as traveling circus entertainers, are approached by a masterful American con man, Michael Nash (Conway Tearle). He sees potential in Zara (Aileen Pringle), telling her, "You're beautiful! You're dazzling! In America you'd be a sensation!" Nash sweet-talks Zara, her father "Poppa" Zazarack (Mitchell Lewis) and knife-thrower Anton (Robert Ober) into coming to America with him. They set up shop in a ritzy New York apartment and Nash publicizes Zara as a famous Hungarian mystic.

Here Browning draws upon his formative experiences in actual sideshows to reveal the techniques used by these circus performers to fool their victims. Nash finds suckers among New York's moneyed class; Zara pretends to go into trances; Zazarack acts as a fast-talking host-cum-distraction during séances, making certain everything goes smoothly and their techniques are not revealed; and Anton, dressed in an all-black outfit, slips into the room via a secret panel and creates the illusion of spectral manifestations.

Despite the fact that the police are keeping an eye on them, Nash decides to pull off their biggest con yet. He learns that Wall Streeter James Bradshaw (David Torrence) has fallen on hard times and has been secretly stealing from his ward, Doris Merrick (Gladys Hulette), left in Bradshaw's care by Doris' deceased father. During one of the phony séances, an illusion that appears to be the ghost of Doris' father materializes. The "spirit" (actually Anton) reveals Bradshaw's crimes to the girl and pleads with her to place her money and valuables in Nash's care. Believing this to be the wish of her dead father, Doris obeys. Nash and his compatriots, of course, plan to skip town with her riches.

This con later becomes complicated when Doris claims to see her father's ghost while in Nash's presence. Nash sees nothing, and yet he senses sincerity in Doris' voice. *She* believes she has seen her father's ghost. It's clear that Nash is spooked by this incident. He's not entirely certain she *hasn't* seen her father's ghost. Once again, the thin line

Gypsy entertainers Mitchell Lewis (with knife),
his daughter Aileen Pringle (blindfolded in box)
and knife-thrower Robert Ober put on a show for
Hungarian villagers in the opening reel of *The Mystic*.
The sign overhead asks, "Do the dead come back?"

gnaws at him and he decides he doesn't want to go through with the con. He tells Zara that he loves her, and that he intends to return Doris' valuables to her. Zara, knowing Nash is a born con man, doesn't believe him. She's convinced that he has fallen in love with Doris. Out of jealousy, she pulls a gun and threatens to kill him unless he agrees to go through with the con. Nash doesn't flinch, fearlessly telling Zara she can't pull the trigger because she knows he's telling the truth. Zara is convinced, but Zazarack and Anton don't agree. They think Nash is planning to steal all the girl's riches for himself. Quickly, we see how a life of lies begets nothing except perpetual distrust.

In the hands of a lesser storyteller, *The Mystic* might have descended into a moralistic fable about the dangers of lying. But Browning's worldview is far more complicated than that. The same trickery that Nash has used to steal thousands of dollars — a police inspector (DeWitt Jennings) calls him the "cleverest crook in America" — is now put to use saving Doris from people who learned all their tricks from Nash himself. When the police close in on Nash and his partners, Nash pretends to use Doris as a human shield in order to buy enough time to slip through the secret panel and get away. He does this so that the police will think he was the crook and that the gypsies were his dupes. Soon after, Nash slips into Doris' bedroom and leaves her valuables on the bed where she's sleeping, along with a note explaining that he needed to con the police into thinking he alone was responsible in order to get Zara and the others off the hook. This is how Browning's brain works: To clear the names of three lifelong cons, a fake con man has successfully conned the police into believing he's a *genuine* con man in order to reverse the results of the con he himself created.

Confused yet? If not, the sideshow trickster in Browning would probably be disappointed.

between trickery and truth is blurred in Browning's sideshow universe. Sometimes we can believe something so intensely that we manifest it in reality. Is this what Doris has done? Even more disturbing is the possibility that Nash and his friends have somehow summoned the ghost of Doris' father through their own efforts. If you do something long enough, even if you're just pretending, sometimes you find that you've become exactly what you were pretending to be. Has Zara unintentionally summoned a genuine ghost?

The uncertainty of all this affects Nash deeply. Perhaps for the first time in his life, his conscience

Tod Browning (literally) oversees John Gilbert and Renée Adorée in *The Show*.

3. *The Show* (1927)

The Show revolves around a love triangle between Cock Robin (John Gilbert), Salome (Renée Adorée) and the Greek (Lionel Barrymore). Cock Robin is an unscrupulous sideshow barker whose charm and good looks enable him to manipulate the gullible crowds. He's equally adept at manipulating the numerous women in his life, most of whom he's more than happy to exploit for their money. The Greek is even more unscrupulous. He attains his money not through manipulation but outright murder. In fact, the Greek kills the father of Robin's latest conquest. Robin, blamed for the murder, hides from the police in the attic above Salome's apartment. While hidden away in this small space, Robin learns that Salome has developed a strange relationship with the old blind man next door. Every day he comes to her apartment to have

her read the latest letters that have arrived from his son, who went off to fight in the war. Robin listens as Salome reads these letters about the heights of glory the son has attained in battle. These letters are the only bright spots in the old man's life, the only thing keeping him alive.

Robin later discovers that the son is not in the war at all. He's condemned to be hanged in the prison right across the street from the apartment building. Salome has been writing and sending these letters herself, to prevent the old man from dying of depression. Robin is forced to pretend to be the son, just back from the war, to keep the lie going. Robin is so overwhelmed by the lengths to which Salome went to brighten the old man's life that he realizes how much harm he has caused with his lies. In contrast, Salome's lies appear to be the act of a saint. In other words, Salome's lies are Vonnegut-esque *foma*. By the end of the film, the Greek's lies and unscrupulous behavior backfire on him in a deadly

Browning and Lon Chaney look to be in deep discussion in this behind-the-scenes shot from *The Unknown*.

manner, while Robin and Salome are allowed to go back to doing their act at the sideshow. *The Show*, at its heart, is once again an examination of the difference between *foma* and deception.

4. The Unknown (1927)

The Unknown, which was almost certainly a major influence on such later sideshow-themed films as Alejandro Jodorowsky's *Santa Sangre* (1989), is also a film about illusions built upon illusions. Knife thrower Alonzo appears to have no arms, but this is just an elaborate form of sideshow trickery. He must pretend to the world to be armless because he's wanted for murder. A unique deformity, double thumbs, would reveal his true identity if anyone was ever allowed to see his hands. In a tragic twist of fate emblematic of the ironic world Browning and Chaney's characters inhabit, Alonzo

falls in love with a beautiful young carnival performer named Nanon (Joan Crawford, a teenager at the time this film was made). Malabar (Norman Kerry) the strongman is loves Nanon, but the girl has a phobia of being held and only feels comfortable around the armless Alonzo. Alonzo knows he cannot reveal his secret to the girl, so he goes to extreme lengths in order to secure Nanon's love. He leaves town and manipulates a surgeon into amputating both of his arms. While Alonzo's away, Malabar's genuine love for Nanon enables the girl to get over her fear of being held. When Nanon reveals this breakthrough to Alonzo, he laughs and cries hysterically at the same time in a scene that's almost unbearably disturbing. Filled with hatred for Malabar, Alonzo schemes to get his revenge on the strongman and to win back Nanon love, but his plot will backfire on him.

Like *West of Zanzibar*, *The Unknown* is a trip into the deepest parts of Hell — in the form of a twisted man's psyche. Browning and Chaney, our tour guides, do everything they can to make us feel as uncomfortable and as nervous as possible as the tour descends into the innermost rings of the sub-conscious. There's no Vonnegut-esque *foma* to be found in this story. For Alonzo, all lies dissolve into darkness.

5. *West of Zanzibar* (1928)

In the title locale, Lon Chaney portrays a magician named Phroso (which is also the name Browning will later give the clown in *Freaks*), who is so eaten away by the desire for revenge that he weaves a complex web of lies and illusions for the purpose of getting back at the man who stole his wife many years before. All of these lies boomerang back on Phroso in such a tragic manner that the

Lon Chaney wore a duck costume in a *West of Zanzibar* scene that landed on the cutting room floor. Several years later, Browning (the one *not* in a duck costume) used the get-up in *Freaks'* shocking finale.

magician becomes a victim of his own deceptions. The plot of *West of Zanzibar* is permeated by the negative side of lies and manipulation … and yet, in the end, as is almost always the case in the world of Tod Browning, there is redemption. Despite his many sadistic crimes, ultimately Phroso uses his talent for conjuring masterful illusions to right the wrongs he has committed over the course of many years. Though no single act could ever counter the severity of Phroso's crimes, his skills as an illusionist save the lives of the people he has come to care for even more than his own vengeful desires.

6. *Where East Is East* (1929)

In the final Browning-Chaney collaboration, the dichotomy between positive and negative lies plays out yet again, this time against the exotic backdrop of Laotian jungles where Tiger Haynes (Lon Chaney in scarface makeup) earns his living trapping wild animals for a circus. When his high-spirited daughter Toyo (Lupe Velez) falls in love with Bobby Bailey, son of the circus owner, Tiger is very displeased. Tiger and Toyo have a close relationship, and Tiger doesn't want to see it end. But Bobby proves himself to Tiger by helping him save Toyo from an escaped tiger. Alas, as in any Browning-Chaney collaboration, tragedy soon strikes — this time courtesy of Toyo's mother, Madame de Sylva (Estelle Taylor), the ultimate femme fatale. (One can't help but wonder if Milton Caniff's famous Dragon Lady, the Asian seductress from the 1930s *Terry and the Pirates* comic strip, was partly based on this character.)

De Sylva decides to steal her daughter's fiancé to get revenge on her former lover Tiger, to whom Toyo's happiness means everything. She seduces Bobby and maintains an almost supernatural grip on his psyche. We watch Bobby's slow mental disintegration as he attempts, with no success, to shake off her influence. Tiger strives to conceal de Sylva's manipulative nature from Toyo, as he has never wanted his daughter to know the painful truth about her mother. He also conceals from her the full extent of de Sylva's relationship with Bobby. Throughout the film, Tiger lies to Toyo to spare her, while de Sylva lies to Toyo to destroy her.

In the end, Tiger knows the only way he can save Bobby and Toyo from de Sylva is to get rid of his former lover once and for all. Earlier in the film, it was established that Rangho, a caged gorilla, hates de Sylva; as Tiger says, "Gorillas never forget those who hurt them!" One evening, Tiger releases Rangho from her cage; once the go-

rilla enters de Sylva's bedroom and sees her, Tiger, Toyo and Bobby's collective problem is solved. Tiger implies that Rangho's escape was an accident, then tells Toyo and Bobby to stay out of harm's way while he deals with Rangho.

At Toyo and Bobby's wedding, Tiger conceals the severity of the wounds he received from

"Not good entertainment!" P.S. Harrison of *Harrison's Reports* bristled. "In *Where East Is East*, the main feature is the hero's letting loose of a gorilla on his ex-wife, mother of the heroine, tearing her to pieces. The actual killing is not, of course, shown; it is only implied. But the thought is there. And it is an unpleasant thought."

Police Inspector Bela Lugosi (how often do you see *that* in print?) charges Leila Hyams with murder, as Margaret Wycherley protests, in *The Thirteenth Chair*.

Rangho so that Toyo will not be burdened by grief on her honeymoon. It's implied that Tiger passes away soon after the ceremony. Once again, Tiger's lies emerge from his intense love for his daughter as opposed to the hateful deceptions woven by de Sylva out of her twisted desire for revenge.

7. *The Thirteenth Chair* (1929)

Five months after the release of *Where East Is East*, Tod Browning debuted a new film just in time for the Halloween season: the eerie murder mystery *The Thirteenth Chair*, adapted from a 1916 stage play by Bayard Veiller. In this film, set in Calcutta, Browning presents to his audience multiple layers of deceptions. Edward Wales (John Davidson) attempts to solve the murder of his best friend, Spencer Lee, by hiring a fake medium, Madame La Grange (Margaret Wycherly), to scare the guilty

party into a confession. During a séance, as La Grange is about to utter the name of the woman Wales suspects is the murderer, Wales screams in pain. When the lights are turned up on the séance, Wales is discovered dead, but the knife is nowhere to be found. Inspector Delzante (Bela Lugosi) soon appears on the scene, intent on finding the murder weapon, which he knows must be hidden somewhere in the room where Wales was murdered.

Here Browning is very clever. The techniques he uses to film the story mirror the plot itself. For example, just before La Grange begins the séance, she demonstrates all the various tricks that mediums use to simulate ghostly manifestations. This is quite similar to *The Mystic*, in which Browning goes out of his way to show the audience how such trickery is actually performed behind the scenes. In this case, La Grange reveals her tricks not to convince her audience that she's a fake, but the exact opposite. It's a prime case of reverse psychology. By revealing herself as a fraud from the very beginning, she knows her audience will believe in the supernatural events that seem to occur during the séance she has been hired to perform. Once again, a major character uses trickery as a means of getting at the truth. And yet, in this case, it's only a half-truth. La Grange has not bothered to reveal the fact that Wales has hired her to fake a supernatural occurrence in order to scare the guilty party into a confession. Though she uses trickery to reveal the facts, it's only a mask for further trickery — the ultimate intent of which is to discover the truth.

Just like Madame La Grange, Browning reveals his own trickery for all to see before Inspector Delzante's investigation gets underway. At the beginning of the scene in which Delzante arrives and begins his relentless questioning of the guests, we see an overhead shot of the entire room. For a moment, the audience can clearly see a knife imbedded in the ceiling. A careful observer would realize that this is the murder weapon for which Delzante will be furiously searching. But how many careful observers are there in any average movie house? Browning is betting that there aren't any at all, i.e., the same number of "careful observers" who gathered for the fake séance in the film. After revealing the location of the murder weapon, the camera tilts down and closes in on Delzante interrogating Sir Roscoe Crosby (Holmes Herbert). Browning knows the audience is so swept up in the plot, so hypnotized by the theatrics, that they will not see what's been placed right in front of them. In this sense, Browning is following the principles of Edgar Allan Poe as laid out in his classic 1844 short story "The Purloined Letter," in which a black-mailer hides from the police a missive that could incriminate members of the royal family by placing it in a letter holder sitting on a mantle, right out in the open where anyone could find it. In fact, Poe and Browning's views about illusions and trickery are so well aligned, it's a shame that Browning nev-

er got around to adapting one of Poe's celebrated Auguste Dupin detective stories.

The remainder of the film is dominated by Lugosi's fierce performance as Delzante and makes one wonder how Lugosi would have fared as a detective character later in his career. (According to Tom Weaver's book *Poverty Row Horrors!*, Monogram producer Sam Katzman considered featuring Lugosi in an adaptation of the Poe mystery story "The Gold Bug," which certainly would have been fascinating to see.) We see Delzante use trickery several times in an attempt to uncover the truth of the situation. First he asks the men of the house to move the corpse to see who will hesitate, but alas, every one of the men hesitates. Delzante reveals he doesn't want the body moved; this was just a test, to observe their reactions. Later, Delzante says that the fingerprints of Helen O'Neill (Leila Hyams, who will later portray Venus the seal trainer in *Freaks*) have been found on a porcelain cup in Spencer Lee's bedroom. Helen responds, "I never touched a cup," unintentionally revealing the fact that she had indeed visited Lee's bedroom. Delzante admits that her fingerprints had not been found in the room at all. As so often happens in Browning's universe, such tricks eventually lead to the truth … or something closely akin to the truth.

As in *The Mystic*, at a crucial moment in the narrative, a touch of the supernatural seems to intrude upon the carefully crafted reality established up to this point. In *The Mystic*, Doris Merrick appears to see the ghost of her deceased father. No one else sees the manifestation, but Michael Nash is unnerved enough to consider the reality of Doris' sighting. In *The Thirteenth Chair*, La Grange admits to herself (and whatever deity might be listening) that she's been a faker her entire life, but prays for an actual communication from the dead in order to help her solve the crime. She hears two raps in the otherwise empty room and interprets them as a sign from beyond. Within moments, we learn that the two raps were actually Delzante signaling La Grange that her time was up. La Grange, resilient as ever, decides to accept Delzante's knocks as meaningful omens nonetheless. The message she attributes to the knocks does indeed help the old woman solve the crime. In other words, La Grange chooses to deceive herself, and this self-deceit unveils a truth that even a professional detective, Delzante, could not uncover on his own. Furthermore, the macabre plan that La Grange dreams up as a result of the knocks — restaging the séance with Wales' corpse taking part in the proceedings — actually does force the murderer to confess. Her lifetime of fakery, a source of shame for her earlier in the narrative, ends up being what Delzante needs to discern the truth.

8. *Dracula* (1931)

So much has been written about the 1931 *Dracula* that one might think there's nothing left to say; however, the critical drubbing this film has received from film fans and critics alike during the past few decades demands a counterargument from an impeccable informed source. Fortunately, such a source arrived in 2015 in the form of Gary D. Rhodes' revelatory book *Tod Browning's* Dracula.

Ahead of its publication, an excerpt appeared in James Clatterbaugh's consistently insightful magazine *Monsters from the Vault* (#29), under the title "The Curious Undead Life of Tod Browning's *Dracula*." Much of what impressed me about that article applies to Rhodes' book-length version as well. For a variety of improbable reasons, Browning's *Dracula* has become one of the most misunderstood and underappreciated films produced in that seminal decade of the 1930s. As mentioned earlier, though the film's influence is vast and undeniable, in recent years critics have used up countless reams of paper and hundreds of thousands of words in their attempts to prove that the film is an artistic failure. Since the beginning of the 1990s, there has been a trend among professional cinema scholars, as well as among amateur film buffs, to establish George Melford's Spanish version of *Dracula* (produced at Universal concurrently with Browning's film) is a superior adaptation of Bram Stoker's supernatural novel. In fact, this was one of the core points of David Skal's book *Hollywood Gothic*. Tellingly, in 2017, Universal released a trailer for their proposed "shared universe" series of monster films, *Dark Universe*. This trailer was composed of iconic shots from Universal's most famous horror films. Instead of using scenes from Browning's *Dracula*, it incorporated only lesser-known shots from the Spanish *Dracula*. It's as if someone at Universal was trying to nudge both Browning and Lugosi out of existence.

In *Hollywood Gothic*, Skal insists that Melford's *Dracula* is far more experimental cinematically than Browning's version, which is accused of being far too stage-bound and theatrical. A claim that Skal often makes to back up this viewpoint is that Melford's film utilizes the moving camera far more than Browning's version. This and other overused examples are, more often than not, based on misperceptions or outright falsehoods.

Back in 2011, when I was about a quarter of the way through Rhodes' original article, this thought suddenly popped into my head: "I've been waiting 20 years for someone to write an article like this." Why 20 years? At the time of the article's publication, it had been about two decades since the publication of *Hollywood Gothic*. Though I appreciate Skal's unique approach to film history (and I love his follow-up book, *The Monster Show*, even more), I suspect his stance regarding the Melford *Dracula* was born more out of narrative necessity than out of genuine conviction. The idea of a lost classic emerging out of the shadow of its far more famous counterpart is a romantic notion and makes for a wonderful story arc too perfect to resist. Also, the Melford *Dracula* wasn't readily available at the time of *Hollywood Gothic*'s publication, so if you were a casual reader and not a film scholar, you had to take Skal's word for it. I did so at the time, as did many of Skal's readers. In the years since, I've grown more and more perplexed over the unthinking hostility directed toward Browning's *Dracula*.

Based on comments that Ray Bradbury made in his *Monsters from the Vault* interview, one would have to conclude that he shared this opinion. He had this to say about the impact Browning's film had on him as a child:

> *Dracula* was a beauty because it was so understated. The use of visual metaphor in the slow buildup of those early scenes is simply

109-1 76

Mina Seward (Helen Chandler) answers Count
Dracula's (Bela Lugosi) supernatural summons.

breathtaking, especially when Bela Lugosi leads Renfield up the stairway of Dracula's castle toward this massive cobweb that stretches all the way across the top of the stairway. When Dracula reaches the top, he passes right through the cobweb without breaking it. That might seem like a simple little trick today, done with just a simple cutaway of editing, but it's still a startling effect. That moment becomes even more re-markable a few seconds later, when Renfield has to break through the cobweb to follow Dracula to the top of the stairs. It's a single strange, eerie moment that you remember forever.

My childhood impression of the film remains, like Bradbury's, unaltered; I've always found Browning's film effectively eerie, not just in its first reel, but throughout its entire 75 minutes. It took Rhodes to point out, at long last, that those

elements of Browning's film habitually accused of being far too stage-bound are, in fact, some of its most effective scenes. After all, the haunting im-ages created in one's imagination when hearing Renfield (memorably portrayed by Dwight Frye) hiss out the words, "Rats … rats … thousands, *mil-lions* of them," are far more disturbing than *show-ing* such an image through the use of base special effects.

In *Tod Browning's Dracula*, Rhodes demonstrat-ed that his conclusions are not in any way subjec-tive; they're a product of pure mathematics, e.g., a matter of simply *counting* how many shots in the Browning film utilize a moving camera as opposed to the Melford version. He then underscores how much more artistically — from a thematic point of view — Browning employs the moving camera as opposed to Melford.

But *Tod Browning's Dracula* is about far more than just comparing and contrasting two films from the 1930s; at its core, the book is about *perceptual psychology*, and the fact that human beings (if told something often enough and with great conviction) tend to believe unfounded claims without first examining their validity. Pretty soon an unsupported claim becomes a possibility, and a possibility becomes a fact, and a fact becomes common knowledge. Rhodes' book upends all the rumors and "what if"s and chimerical half-truths and shines the light of genuine scholarship on the facts underlying the lies that have shrouded this historically important film.

Once again, we've hit upon the theme of truth emerging from lies. In this case, this theme spills out of the frame of Browning's film and invades, meta-like, the consciousness of the real world. Is this the ultimate magic trick? For this reason, among others, I think the sideshow trickster in Browning would be quite amused by the heated debate his most famous film has instigated.

9. Freaks (1932)

Dracula was one of Browning's most successful films at the time of its release. What's fascinating is that a couple of the Browning's films that were *un*popular upon release have emerged as some of the most forward-thinking and influential films of the 1930s. For example, one could easily make the argument that *Freaks* (1932), based on Tod Robbins' 1923 short story "Spurs," is one of the most daring and revolutionary films of the Golden Age of Hollywood — and without a doubt one of the most influential. The list of artistic works that contain the DNA of *Freaks* is long, varied and most impressive: Charles G. Finney's *The Circus of Dr. Lao* (1935), William Lindsay Gresham's *Nightmare Alley* (1946), Ray Bradbury's *Dark Carnival* (1947), *The Illustrated Man* (1951), *The October Country* (1955) and *Something Wicked This Way Comes* (1962), Edmund Goulding's *Nightmare Alley* (1947), Federico Fellini's *La Strada* (1954) and

Satyricon (1969), Max Ophüls' *Lola Montès* (1955), Luis Bunuel's *Viridiana* (1961), Ed Wood's *Killer in Drag* (1965), Ingmar Bergman's *Hour of the Wolf* (1968), Alejandro Jodorowsky's *El Topo* (1970) and *Santa Sangre* (1989), Bill Griffith's *Zippy the Pinhead* (1971–the present) and *Nobody's Fool: The Life and Times of Schlitzie the Pinhead* (2019), Len Wein and Bernie Wrightson's *Swamp Thing* (1972-76), Dennis Etchison's "On the Pike" (1977) (which can be found in Etchison's 1984 short story collection, *Red Dreams*), David Lynch's *Eraserhead* (1977), the Ramones' *Leave Home* (1977), Bruce Jones and Bernie Wrightson's *Freak Show* (1982), Angela Carter's *Nights at the Circus* (1984), Katherine Dunn's *Geek Love* (1989), Woody Allen's *Shadows and Fog* (1991), Daniel Knauf's *Carnivàle* (2003-2005), Ryan Murphy and Brad Falchuk's *American Horror Story: Freak Show* (2014-15), Guillermo del Toro's *Nightmare Alley* (2021), the photographs of Diane Arbus, the surrealist paintings of Leonora Carrington, and (if I might be allowed a moment of self-indulgence), my own fiction, particularly my 2006 short story "Feast of Clowns" (which was first published in W.H. Horner's anthology *Modern Magic: Tales of Fantasy and Horror*).

On his *Freaks* DVD audio commentary, David Skal called it the "ultimate cult movie." One could argue that the entire "psychotronic" cinematic subculture grew out of this single film. *Freaks* horrified moviegoers worldwide because of its unrelenting desire to shove into the faces of viewers the most discomfiting reality of all — not the make-believe Hollywood horror of Lon Chaney's *The Phantom of the Opera*, but the stark deformities that exist in the real world. Tod Browning showed the world the line that separates the normal from the abnormal, but the world did not wish to be reminded of how thin that line *is*. Most of the world rejected the film — that is, until the 1960s, when a new wave of overeager filmmakers began to dominate Hollywood, a revolutionary generation who wished to explore the uncomfortable worlds of reality over the saccharine Hollywood fantasies on which they had been weaned. The raw and gritty visions of some of these young filmmakers, like Francis Ford Coppola and Martin Scorsese, were inevitably absorbed by the mainstream, while others, like Herk Harvey and John

"What are you, a man or a baby?": Cleopatra (Olga Baclanova) dresses down her new husband Hans (Harry Earles) in front of Hercules (Henry Victor).

Waters, had to create their own films on the outer edges of the industry. The iconoclastic imaginations of these filmmakers helped fill the vast void created by the absence of Browning, from which Hollywood had been suffering since the backlash to *Freaks*. It was Browning's ghost, the example laid down by the transgressive spirit of *Freaks* and its unusual stars, that each of these young filmmakers were following, whether they realized it or not.

Like Browning's other films, *Freaks* dramatizes fascination with deception and the consequences thereof. Circus trapeze artist Cleopatra (Olga Baclanova) and strongman Hercules (Henry Victor) conspire to steal the inherited fortune of a dwarf named Hans (Harry Earles). Cleopatra pretends to be in love with Hans and manipulates him into proposing to her, then proceeds to poison him slowly. The other sideshow freaks uncover Cleopatra's deception and mete out a little well-deserved "freak justice." We can only assume that Hercules is

killed by the vengeful, knife-wielding freaks while Cleopatra has her legs cut off, her face disfigured, and her throat destroyed. At the end of the film, we see that the once beautiful trapeze performer has been stuffed into a duck costume and forced to perform in the sideshow as the most repulsive freak of all.

Throughout the film, Browning's sympathies clearly lie with the freaks. But ever since its release, Browning has been accused of having exploited the freaks featured in the movie, of casting them in a nightmarish light. It's hard to imagine anyone who has actually seen the film coming to this conclusion. The climactic scene in which the freaks pursue Cleopatra and Hercules through the stormy darkness of night is certainly horrific, but not because of the freaks themselves. The freaks are forced to handle the situation in the only way they know. None of the violence depicted on the screen needed to occur in the first place. The violence only happens due to the cruel acts of the so-called normal people in the film, Cleopatra and Hercules.

As Carlos Clarens writes in his groundbreaking 1967 book *An Illustrated History of the Horror Film*:

> Browning also takes a compassionate look into the private lives of his creatures and finds them to be sensitive, vulnerable, and intensely human characters. His camera descends to their level: one effective scene between two midgets, surrounded by their tiny props, communicates a sense of normality that is destroyed when a normal person intrudes on the scene. Freaks among themselves cease to be freaks.

That last sentence sums up the basic theme of Browning's film. In the context of his other work, it makes sense that Browning is sympathetic to the freaks and their day-to-day plight. After all, the freaks are among the few characters in a Browning film who do not live to deceive others. They might be the most honest characters to ever populate Browning's universe. Though the freaks do regularly indulge in Vonnegut-esque *fomas* for showmanship reasons, to enhance their disabilities for the purposes of entertainment, nonetheless they are the only people in Browning's world who are not trying to hide who they are inside. Of course, they wouldn't be able to hide even if they wanted to do so. In this sense, the freaks' various disabilities force them to live a life of honesty with very little pretense. They are actually going out of their way to advertise and capitalize on what separates them from the rest of humanity. Like the alchemists of old, they have managed to transform base lead into gold; they have turned a disadvantage into a way of life that works for them all. Their only indulgences in the art of deception are the kind that Browning perceives as being positive, necessary accoutrements to the life of a born showman.

Appropriately enough, the topic of lies and hon-

esty is broached in the very first line spoken in the film: "We didn't lie to you, folks! We told you we had living, breathing monstrosities. You laughed at them, shuddered at them — and yet, but for the accident of birth, you might be even as they are. They did not ask to be brought into the world, but into the world they came…." Not so strangely, this last line could apply to almost all of Browning's characters.

10. *Mark of the Vampire* (1935)

Like most horror cinema fans, I was disappointed with Browning's *Mark of the Vampire*, but I have since come to adore the film. Aside from *Dracula*, it's probably the Browning film I've seen the most. As film historian Gregory William Mank writes in his 1993 book *Hollywood Cauldron*, this can be

> a lonely time to be a Tod Browning fan. This former carnival geek/circus ringmaster/blackface vaudevillian/D.W. Griffith assistant/Poe of the screen has been suffering some hard knocks for his stodgy cinema style and a pace as slow and scuttly as those armadillos that inexplicably upstage Lugosi's entrance in *Dracula*. When one learns of Browning's life, it is perhaps not surprising that many of his films unspool like an alcoholic's nightmare; confused, sick, sordid, muddled, populated by rats and bugs (and armadillos). Nor is it surprising that among film historians–critics, the armadillo hunt is on and has become an open season sport.

> "More often than not," wrote David J. Skal in *Hollywood Gothic*, "the Browning end product is an unholy mess. There is no denying, however, the enduring fascination of his work, even if the fascination is akin to watching an auto wreck." In their 1990 tome *Universal Horrors*, John Brunas, Michael Brunas and Tom Weaver (who coined the now-popular term "Browning-bashing") slap the Browning "rediscoveries" as "turgid, plotty bores, each representing one more nail in the once-fabled director's critical coffin."

This mass-mind–inspired hostility is as mystifying as the tricks on display in Browning's sideshow universe. If Browning's best films are tantamount to auto wrecks, more directors should be willing to ram their vehicles into large stationary objects. There's much to admire in Browning's psychologically complex oeuvre, and even when the director is not playing his A-game, there's still much to enjoy in his work.

Mark of the Vampire is the surviving version of the most infamous lost film of all time, Browning and Chaney's *London After Midnight* (1927). It boasts wonderful cinematography by James Wong Howe, who would later win Academy Awards for his work on *The Rose Tattoo* (1955) and *Hud* (1963). It features a fine cast of strong character actors all attempting to upstage each other in subtle ways, a struggle that's always fun to watch. Lionel Barrymore, Bela Lugosi, Lionel Atwill, Jean Hersholt, Holmes Herbert, Elizabeth Allan and Carroll Borland all make lasting impressions in the viewer's mind. And Lugosi and Borland somehow manage to steal the show without uttering more than a few words between them.

The plot is convoluted, to say the least. The disappointment experienced by most horror film fans upon first seeing *Mark of the Vampire* stems mainly from the revelation at the end: that the supernatural phenomena we've seen throughout the story were, in fact, an elaborate hoax staged by actors in order to frighten a confession out of Baron Otto von Zinden (Hersholt). A year earlier, the baron murdered Sir Karell Borotyn (Herbert), father of Irena (Allan). Von Zinden is so madly in love with her that he poisoned Sir Karell in order to prevent Irena's marriage to Fedor Vincente (Henry Wadsworth). Von Zinden went so far as to drain Sir Karell's body of blood in order to make it appear that vampires had killed him.

It's fascinating to watch the film from the perspective of Prof. Zelen (Barrymore) and Inspector Neumann (Atwill), the men responsible for hatching this overly complicated psyop. It's equally fun trying to back-engineer the thought processes of the screenwriters of both *London After Midnight* and *Mark of the Vampire*. Attempt to imagine what was in their minds when they were constructing

this bewildering narrative. From the ending of *Mark*, it's clear that Fedor, Maria the maid (Leila Bennett) and Dr. Doskil (Donald Meek) are the only three major characters unaware that the vampires roaming the countryside are merely actors. Prof. Zelen, Inspector Neumann, Irena, Jan the butler (Ivan Simpson) and the actors playing the vampires (Bela Lugosi and Carroll Borland) are all in on the plot.

Does this mean that Irena went along with the idea of her fiancé being attacked by a couple of actors dressed as vampires at the beginning of the film, or did von Zinden (in the guise of a vampire) attack Fedor in an attempt to get him out of the way? This latter theory is supported by a comment made by the actor portraying Irena's dead father near the end of the film: He says to Irena, "After the attack on Mr. Vincenty, it was *you* who first suspected von Zinden of the crime." This seems to suggest that the scheme to play with von Zinden's mind was not conceived until *after* Fedor was waylaid … but were his attackers real vampires, or was von Zinden to blame?

Untangling *Mark of the Vampire*'s plot can be challenging, to say the least. Numerous supernatural events are captured by the objective eye of the camera with no one around to observe them. For example, in their first scene together, Count Mora and Luna walk right through a massive spider web without disturbing it. How did two stage actors manage to pull that off? And if it was a trick, why did they perform it with no one watching? Similarly, we see Luna attack Irena while Mora watches approvingly from the fog. There's no one else around to observe this attack. Are these the most devoted method actors in existence? (Perhaps these roving actors were graduates of Lee Strasberg's Group Theatre in New York, formed only five years before *Mark of the Vampire*'s release, where "the Method" was first made popular.) Or have Irena and Luna developed a somewhat fetishistic relationship that extends far beyond the professional? Is this the *real* reason Irena seems so guilt-ridden whenever she's alone with her fiancé? I wouldn't be surprised if Irena ran off with Luna and her fascinating troupe after the final fade-out. If so … too bad, Fedor. (Remember that for future reference: Never allow

Bela Lugosi and teenage Carroll Borland enact
a *Mark of the Vampire* scene under Browning's
watchful eye.

your fiancée to carouse with actor-vampires after midnight. You never know what might happen.)

In the film's most famous moment, Luna descends from the ceiling of Sir Karell's castle on vast bat wings extended behind her in a surreal, Max Ernst–like fashion. While peering in through the window, Von Zinden just happens to catch a glimpse of this very elaborate stunt. Did Luna and her troupe have that stunt all ready to go on the off-chance that von Zinden might decide to show up at that very window? If so, they are extremely patient thespians.

More delightful conundrums arise to confound the *Mark of the Vampire* devotee: Von Zinden is on hand as his butler Jan describes seeing a bat transform into Count Mora. We see this happen in flashback. Of course, Jan could be lying to frighten von Zinden. We know, based on later events, that Jan is in on the con. However, this explanation is contradicted by the fact that Maria the maid is with him at the time of Mora's transformation and she claims to have seen the same thing. We

know that Maria is *not* aware of the scheme to entrap von Zinden, so does this mean that the actors staged an elaborate transformation of Mora (or, more accurately, the actor playing Mora) from a bat into a human simply to scare a maid who was *already* scared? And how the heck did they make it seem as if Mora transformed from bat to human in the middle of a normal, everyday hallway using the technology that would have been available to vaudevillians in 1935?

The only explanation that makes any sense is that Count Mora and Luna are vampires pretending to be actors pretending to be vampires, perhaps using Edgar Allan Poe's previously quoted principle that it's best to hide in plain sight. How else to reconcile the clearly supernatural events mentioned above with the prosaic explanation at the end of the film?

Another problem: In the final act, Prof. Zelen hypnotizes the baron into reenacting the events that occurred the night of Sir Karell's death. If Zelen had the ability to hypnotize von Zinden all along, why was there a need to frighten the baron into thinking vampires were stalking him? One would presume that Zelen's hypnosis would have revealed von Zinden's guilt with or without the presence of fake vampires. Was it necessary to wear von Zinden down psychologically before he was in a mental state that would be receptive to Zelen's hypnotic techniques? If so, this is yet another plot point that the viewer must fill in for himself.

Mark of the Vampire is, in the end, an interactive film. It continually pushes the viewer out of its carefully constructed reality with paradoxes piled upon paradoxes … paradoxes that appear to have been planted in the film on purpose. After all, *Mark of the Vampire* was a remake of an eight-year-old film. Browning had had years to meditate on this plot, which was based on his own story "The Hypnotist." If there are plot holes in *Mark of the Vampire*, one can only conclude that Browning very much wanted there to be. It's also possible, of course, that these plot holes were far less evident in the original version in which Prof. Zelen, Count Mora and Inspector Neumann were all played by one actor (Chaney). Surely, splitting a single character into three must have caused innumerable problems for the *Mark of the Vampire* screenwriters, problems that may not have been resolved before the script had to go before the cameras. But it's just as possible that *Mark of the Vampire* is Browning's ultimate illusion. It's the cinematic equivalent of a professional magician suddenly deciding to unpack his suitcase of illusions for the astonished crowd and invite them to join in on the fun: "Behold! Here's how I saw a woman in half … and here's how that white rabbit appears to emerge out of nothing…" *Mark of the Vampire* is filled with bizarre conundrums that cannot be explained unless the viewer takes it upon himself to co-write the scenario with the filmmakers. This is close-up magic that invites further inspection from the milling crowd.

In *Mark of the Vampire*'s last scene, Count Mora (in a purposefully self-mocking tone) declares that he gave his performance his all. I suspect that Browning gave *Mark of the Vampire* his all as well. He threw all his tried-and-true secret methods into the laps of audience members, allowing them to sort through it all on their own. *Mark of the Vampire* is an illusion that appears to fail, and yet succeeds in perpetually confounding the audience, thus creating a unique brand of movie magic that frustrates the casual viewer while challenging the more engaged observer with seemingly unexplainable paradoxes that invite further investigation and speculation. *Mark of the Vampire* is an illusion that succeeds while also failing — perhaps the ultimate magic trick. Once again, Browning has woven truth and lies into an inexplicable but compelling pattern that is almost impossible to unravel.

11. *The Devil-Doll* (1936)

The main conflict of *The Devil-Doll*, Browning's penultimate film, also involves the stark contrast between deception and *foma*. Before I saw this film, a friend described it to me as "a cross between *Mrs. Doubtfire*, *The Count of Monte Cristo* and *The Incredible Shrinking Man*." What's most amazing about this description is that it's accurate.

The way-out plot revolves around Paul Lavond (Lionel Barrymore), framed for the crimes of embezzlement and murder by his partners in a Paris bank, Radin (Arthur Hohl), Coulvet (Robert Greig) and Matin (Pedro de Cordoba). The film opens as Lavond, after 17 years on Devil's Island, escapes with an eccentric old scientist named Marcel (Henry B. Walthall). Before Marcel dies, he demonstrates for Lavond his machine that can miniaturize humans and animals.

Accompanied by Marcel's widow Malita (Rafaela Ottiano), Lavond slips into Paris in the guise of an old woman named Madame Mandilip. There the pair open a toy shop, the cover for Lavond's scheme to get revenge on the men who sent him to prison. Lavond uses Marcel's miniaturization machine to reduce Radin in size. A side effect of the process is that it robs the subject of his free will. Lavond uses this to his advantage by employing his

The "living dolls" in *The Devil-Doll* (including Arthur Hohl, pictured here) came to the screen via a combination of special effects and king-sized sets. At one point it was proposed that the living dolls be proportioned and sculptured like real children's dolls, but it was felt that that might spoil the story by creating a comic effect.

"dolls" as remote-controlled avengers. After Radin and Coulvet fall victim, Matin is so panicked at the prospect of becoming the next casualty that he confesses their crimes to the police, clearing Lavond's name.

Though ostensibly based on Abraham Merritt's 1932 fantasy tale *Burn Witch Burn!*, the screenplay by Garrett Fort (who co-wrote Browning's *Dracula*), Guy Endore (who co-wrote *Mark of the Vampire*) and Erich von Stroheim bears little resemblance to the source material. Merritt's novel is an occult fantasy, while Browning's film is presented to the audience as science fiction. One wonders if England's ban on horror films necessitated the changes, just as Universal's *The Invisible Ray* (1936) with Karloff and Lugosi wrapped itself in a cloak of science fiction to sidestep the recent criticisms of horror films such as *The Black Cat* (1934), *The Raven* (1935) and Browning's own *Freaks*.

I suspect that many of the storyline changes came directly from Browning, as the most dramatic alterations shift the plot away from Mer-

ritt's dark fantasy and closer to the crime-suspense genre that Browning had so often explored with Chaney. In fact, many of the plot changes bring the film more in line with past Browning-Chaney successes such as *The Unholy Three*. Once again, a man who's up to no good (Barrymore) dresses as an old woman in order to hide in plain sight as he commits a series of crimes. In both films, small people — Harry Earles in *The Unholy Three* and a shrunken female servant named Lachna (Grace Ford) in *The Devil-Doll* — use their diminutive size as their advantage as they steal jewels from the lavish homes of Madame Mandilip's well-to-do customers. Both films feature a suspenseful scene in which a police inspector visits the cross-dressing criminal's shop due to the fact that "she" had visited the home of the victim the day before.

The most important similarity between *The Devil-Doll* and Browning's past films is the dramatic disparity between positive and negative lies. The plot of *The Devil-Doll* is kicked off by the treachery of Radin, Coulvet and Matin, who push Lavond into prison by creating an enormous lie that boomerangs back on them. Lavond uses lies in both positive and negative ways. He uses lies to cover up his crimes, but he also uses the same lies to clear his name as well as to prevent his adult daughter Lorraine (Maureen O'Sullivan) from experiencing any more pain due to his wrongful imprisonment. Almost her entire life, Lorraine has lived under the weight of her father's disgrace, so much so that she intensely believes in her father's guilt. In the end, after Lavond's innocence has been proven, Lavond pretends to be someone else — the second Devil's Island escapee — as he visits with Lorraine atop the Eiffel Tower, telling her that her father is dead and that she should now move on with her life and feel no guilt over having doubted his innocence. Lavond does this because, as he explains to Lorraine's fiancé Toto (Frank Lawton), Lavond was forced to commit real crimes in order to clear his name of crimes he *didn't* commit. Paradoxically, he feels both vindicated and tainted at the same time — too tainted to try resuming his old life with Lorraine. Thus, once again in Browning's binary universe, lies are used to prevent pain as well as cause it.

12. *Miracles for Sale* (1939)

Appropriately, inevitably, the mixture of truth and lies is a motif that runs throughout Browning's final film *Miracles for Sale* (based on Clayton Rawson's 1938 mystery novel *Death from a Top Hat*). Given the grim nature of Browning's previous offerings, *Miracles for Sale* is surprisingly light and straightforward. *Miracles for Sale* is to Browning what *The Stranger* (1946) was to Orson Welles, what *The Straight Story* (1999) was to David Lynch: an opportunity to prove to the masses that these geniuses of cutting-edge cinema could craft a film with a linear, easy-to-grasp plot just like any other director who can yell "Action!" and "Cut!" This is not to say that *Miracles for Sale*, *The Stranger* and *The Straight Story* are inferior films. Indeed, there's something quite appealing about seeing a taboo-shattering, risk-taking artist attempt a different, more accessible form of communication. Accessibility is not necessarily a burden. For some artists, it can be liberating.

Though *Miracles for Sale* never makes it onto the Top 100 lists of Golden Age thrillers compiled by respectable film scholars, I've always been very fond of it. For a director's final film, it does not feel in any way tired, forced or belabored. It's as if Browning felt confident enough in his skills to relax and allow himself (and a very fine cast) to simply have fun telling an excellent story that nonetheless recapitulates the themes that had haunted Browning for so very long.

Fans of Golden Age cinema, particularly horror film aficionados, will appreciate the cast assembled for this film. Appearances by Henry Hull (star of *WereWolf of London*, 1935), Gloria Holden (star of *Dracula's Daughter*, 1936) and Frank Craven (Harry

Brewster in *Son of Dracula*, 1943) instill in modern horror film fans a welcome feeling of *déjà vu*. The film's star, MGM leading man Robert Young, plays the Amazing Morgan, a magician who makes a very good living creating illusions for other magicians. He's also well-known for exposing fake mediums and the like. This is the main reason he's approached by the beautiful Judy Barclay (Florence Rice, recognizable to devoted Marx Bros. fans as Julie Randall in MGM's same-year *At the Circus*), who begs him to help her debunk the work of medium Madame Rapport (Gloria Holden). Before any such debunking can occur, however, two men — Dr. Sabbatt (Frederic Worlock), a demonologist, and Tauro the Great (Harold Minjir), a magician — are murdered under puzzling circumstances. Police using traditional methods are unable to

crack the case; only the Amazing Morgan, with his expertise in illusions, is capable of revealing the identity of the killer and saving Judy from becoming the third victim.

Since this film is Browning's swan song, it's telling that it begins by fully immersing the audience in an elaborate illusion, thus disorientating them as to where they are in time and space. We begin in what appears to be a war scene, with a beautiful woman's life being threatened by a pack of bloodthirsty soldiers. We soon discover that we've been dropped into the middle of a performance of one of the Amazing Morgan's illusions. Amusingly, once the illusion has been completed, Morgan shouts an order to an unseen stagehand: "You can shut off the war now!" He then informs his client that the complex illusion can be packed up in only five crates. We understand now that Morgan is both a very practical businessman as well as a bit of a show-off. These two aspects of his character inform his actions throughout the rest of the film.

Despite the fact that Morgan has now been established as a master illusionist as well as a realist, we learn during this first scene that he allows for the existence of the supernatural. As he says later in the film, "Plenty of things happen that can't be explained by any of the rules of this world. […] For several thousand years, the human race has been trying to step across the threshold into the darkness of the unknown — call it the Other World, if you like — because there's *something* there, and once in a while somebody gets pretty close to it." The reason Morgan spends so much time debunking fake spiritualists, he explains, is that they detract from the serious researchers who are making a sincere effort to explore genuine supernatural phenomenon. As in *The Mystic* and *The Thirteenth Chair*, a hint of the otherworldly does indeed exist on the periphery of Browning's universe. We may never see any genuine examples of such phenomenon,

but Browning (the former carny and the eternal showman) always leaves open the slight possibility that it exists … somewhere.

Though *Miracles for Sale* was not a commercial success at the time of its release, Morgan's unorthodox methods of using his skills as a magician to back-engineer the illusions and tricks used to obscure the identity of the killer could very well have influenced future artifacts of American pop culture such as Carlton E. Morse's *Adventures by Morse* (a popular radio show in the mid-1940s) and Walter B. Gibson's *Blackstone, the Magic Detective* (who first appeared on radio in 1948), comic book heroes such as Leonard Starr's *Dr. 13* (who first appeared in *Star Spangled Comics* in 1951) and George Kashdan and Leonard Starr's *Mysto, Magician Detective* (who first appeared in 1954 as a back-up character in *Detective Comics*), and television shows such as *Scooby Doo* (1969–the present), *The Magician* (1973-74), *Blacke's Magic* (1986), *F/X: The Series* (1996-1998), *Psych* (2006-2014), and *The Mentalist* (2008-2015). As with *Freaks*, the ripple effects of this initially unsuccessful film can still be felt to this very day.

As Gregory Mank wrote, it is indeed a lonely time to be a Tod Browning admirer. I hope that retrospectives such as this one — in which Browning's films are seen to be part of a larger continuum that deals with serious themes over the course of many works spread out across decades — will allow the casual movie fan as well as the serious scholar to place Browning's work in its proper framework: that of visionary dispatches from the edge of the unknown in which discomfort, lies, and illusions are all woven together in ways that would not be attempted by any mainstream director again for well over three decades and to this very moment has never been duplicated in quite the same way as the taboo-shattering work produced by that ultimate showman of the Golden Age of Hollywood, director-writer-sideshow barker-master illusionist, Tod Browning.

The Browning Version: The Journey of *Freaks* from Page to Screen

by Nathaniel Bell

"Offend one, and you offend them all!" So goes the famous line barked at the outset of *Freaks* (1932), the most notorious of all pre–Code horror films. It's a line that does not exist in the original screenplay, but was added during a period of reshoots ordered by Irving G. Thalberg, the Metro-Goldwyn-Mayer executive in charge of the production. Largely reviled and ignored in its day, *Freaks* is now widely regarded as one of the finest — and certainly one of the least typical — films

ever produced by a major Hollywood studio. Under Tod Browning's vivid direction, the titular circus performers, played by actors with real deformities, are alternatively depicted as sweet, childish, sympathetic, clownish, dignified and, ultimately, terrifyingly "other." MGM often boasted that theirs was the movie studio with "more stars than there are in Heaven," but not even the most liberal moviegoers were adequately prepared to spend such time in the company of these unlikely stars, whose members

Left to right: Tod Browning, Johnny Eck, Frances O'Connor (Armless Girl), Peter Robinson, Elizabeth Green.

include Schlitze the Pinhead, Johnny Eck the Half Boy, Koo Koo the Bird Girl and Prince Randian the Human Torso.

Freaks undertook a long and tortuous journey from print to screen to TV and finally to home video, where it has reclaimed its rightful place in film history. But only its most ardent fans know that what is available to us today is a severely truncated version of a much longer film. Standing at 62 minutes, the *Freaks* that endures in the cultural imagination is roughly one-third shorter than the cut shown to a test audience a few weeks prior to its theatrical release. Fans have often mused about whether the scrapped footage would have added anything of value to the whole. Fortunately, a complete screenplay and two "dialogue cutting continuity scripts" provide us with the answer, clueing us in to what was left on the proverbial cutting room floor. Archived in the core and special collections of the Margaret Herrick Library in Beverly Hills, these manuscripts help us trace the evolution of Browning's unclassifiable classic.

To briefly summarize, *Freaks* began life as a short story in 1923. It was optioned and developed into a full screenplay in 1931, filmed and assembled into a cut running roughly 90 minutes in 1932, and subsequently shorn to 62 minutes for release. Next, exploitation filmmaker Dwain Esper re-cut it into a roadshow edition. *Freaks* became its old, original-theatrical-presentation self again for cable television and home video, where it has lived ever since.

The majority of this chapter will focus on the complete screenplay, dated October 29, 1931. Assuming that most or all of its 107 pages were filmed, we can piece together a clear picture of the movie seen by the test audience in early January 1932. If there hadn't been such intense blowback from the preview audience, we would surely have an even more powerful, suggestive and violent film than we have now.

The two "dialogue cutting continuity scripts" were assembled after the preview screening. They include material recorded during the four days of reshoots under Browning's direction as mandated by Thalberg. While we do not have the modified complete scripts that take into account these extra production days, we can see some of the final changes reflected in the dialogue cutting continuity scripts. The wraparound story with the carnival barker ("Offend one, and you offend them all!") and the happy ending with Hans and Frieda reuniting are the most conspicuous additions. But it was the deletion of material that struck the greatest blow to Browning's original vision. In particular, the extended climax involving a wagon train on a mountain road at night, which sees the freaks exact hideous revenge on Cleo and Hercules, was longer, more elaborately staged, and more transgressive than what ultimately survived the editing process. And the concluding scene in Tetrallini's Music Hall, revealing what happened to Hercules, was purportedly too brutal for pre–Code audiences.

The Short Story (February 1923)

Following the success of Universal's *Dracula*, Irving Thalberg, MGM's 32-year-old production manager, began shopping for intellectual property that could be molded into a bankable horror film. He settled on a short story entitled "Spurs," written by Clarence Allen "Tod" Robbins and originally published in the February 1923 issue of *Munsey's Magazine*.

The narrative is set in France and concerns one M. Jacques Courbe, a dwarf of unusual stature: "He measured only twenty-eight inches from the soles of his diminutive feet to the crown of his head." Jacques loves the normal-sized bareback rider Mlle. Jeanne Marie, "a blonde woman of the Amazon type." His romantic rival is Simon Lafleur, "the Romeo of the circus tent" — a dark and dashing acrobat.

Jacques, who has a reputation for being "ill-tempered and egotistical," has no friends among the other freaks in Copo's Circus. In turn, Jacques "loathed them for their acceptance of things as they were." Jacques' sideshow routine involves riding a dog, St. Eustache, and mimicking the movements of the circus' normal-sized horseback riders. Jacques' uncle, a prosperous farmer, dies and leaves him a large estate. This gives Jacques the confidence to make romantic overtures to Jeanne Marie. Initially, she intends to make sport of him,

"She's the most beautiful big woman I've ever seen!":
Hans (Harry Earles) and Cleopatra (Olga Baclanova)
flirt under the Big Top.

———◦———

but changes her mind once Jacques tells her of his fortune. She marries him hoping that he will die young, yet "she would do nothing to hasten the end of Jacques Courbe."

The wedding feast is attended by Papa Coco the circus owner, Griffo the Giraffe Boy ("who was covered with spots and whose neck was so long that he looked down on all the rest"), M. Hercule Hippo the giant, Mlle. Lupa ("who had sharp white teeth of an incredible length and who growled when she tried to talk"), M. Jejongle, a juggler, and Mme. Samson ("with her trained boa constrictors coiled about her neck and peeping out timidly").

The wedding feast, as in the film, is a memorable set piece, but for different reasons. In "Spurs," the evening descends into a brawl between the champagne-besotted sideshow performers. Now securely married to money, Jeanne Marie drops her act and begins to humiliate Jacques in front of the others, including a jeering Simon.

A year later, Simon is visited by Jeanne Marie, now a worn-out, demoralized version of her former self. She explains that her marriage to Jacques has been miserable. Jacques forces her to carry him on her back while he goads her with spurs. She implores Simon to protect her. But Jacques, riding St. Eustache, interrupts the conversation. He charges at Simon and stabs him to death. Jeanne Marie wearily takes up her wifely duties again.

Browning had been interested in "Spurs" for a number of years prior to its acquisition. Harry Earles, Lon Chaney's co-star in both versions of *The Unholy Three* (*also* based on a Tod Robbins story), had reportedly brought it to his attention. MGM purchased the film rights and Willis Goldbeck and Elliott Clawson were assigned to develop the screenplay. (Goldbeck and Leon Gordon are the only names on the final shooting script.) Additional dialogue by Edgar Allan Woolf, Al Boasberg and Charles MacArthur was incorporated into the screenplay. Boasberg had worked on several Buster Keaton and Harold Lloyd pictures and would later contribute dialogue to *A Night at the Opera* (1935). Woolf subsequently joined the writing team on *The Wizard of Oz* (1939). MacArthur was Ben Hecht's collaborator on *The Front Page* (1931), for which both received considerable acclaim. The ingredients for a memorable horror picture were in place.

The Complete Screenplay (October 29, 1931)

Thalberg okayed a complete version of the script on October 29, 1931, a few weeks prior to the start of principal photography. Jacques, the cruel and ill-tempered dwarf, became Hans, a successful yet sweetly naïve midget. He and Frieda, his equally diminutive colleague, are deeply in love. But Hans falls for the tall, voluptuous Cleopatra, an evolution of the Jeanne Marie character. When Cleo and her lover Hercules, an arrogant and brutish circus strongman, learn that Hans has inherited a fortune, they conspire to marry Cleo to Hans and then slowly poison him with ptomaine. But Hans discovers the plot, and he, along with the other freaks, initiate unspeakable revenge.

The script also introduces two key characters, Venus and Phroso, a "normal" couple presumably added to provide audiences with comforting identification figures. A second romantic triangle emerges. These characters, featured prominently in the original screenplay, were later cut down drastically.

The following excerpts highlight the most significant portions of the original screenplay that were either heavily edited or cut entirely. Rather

"I like to take them into the sunshine": The freaks frolic in the forest. Background: Elvira Snow, Jenny Lee Snow, Elizabeth Green, Schlitze. Foreground: Johnny Eck, Peter Robinson, Angelo Rossitto.

than make a comprehensive list of alterations, which would introduce difficulties in presentation and challenge the patience of the reader, the present writer provides a selection of scenes judged to be of the most interest to fans and scholars.

The Scene in the Woods

Viewers will recall the early scene in which the freaks are shown frolicking in the woods. Their encampment lies on private property, and the landowner (Albert Conti) arrives to investigate his caretaker's (Michael Visaroff) report that "a lot of horrible, twisted things" have trespassed. The freaks are protected by Madame Tetrallini ("a vigorous, normal, motherly French woman"), who refers to

them as her "children." In the original complete screenplay, this forest scene opens the film. The caretaker hears music, "as though Pan were piping somewhere there in the green shadows."

In the foreground, the Human Skeleton is lying on his back in the lush grass, smiling up at the sky. Little Martha, a girl with four-inch legs and no arms, dances about him. Little Angeleno, a distorted dwarf, is dancing with her, strewing the Human Skeleton with wild flowers. Little Martha is singing in a high, cracked voice as she dances. John George is playing on the ocarina: "Call me early, mother dear…"

Schlitze is pulling the petals from a daisy and chanting: "He loves me, he loves me not…"

The camera moves over to the Bearded Lady, who is seated on a mossy rock, diligently sewing on tiny garments while her foot keeps time with the music. Rockie and Mamie, the Siamese twins, are laughing and dancing while Cuckoo the Bird Girl skips around them. Madame Tetrallini is wading in the brook, playfully bobbing the turtle girl, born with fleshy flippers instead of arms and legs, up and down in the water.

The landowner and caretaker, appalled, order the freaks to move along. But Tetrallini's response softens their hearts, and they apologize. Tetrallini sends Angeleno to go and fetch Hans and Frieda, who are missing.

Hans and Frieda

In the October 29 screenplay, Hans and Frieda are first seen in the woods. Hans is dressed in white flannels with a smart sport coat, carrying a stick.

Frieda wears a dainty little French afternoon frock, with a parasol. Frieda opines in German: "Ach! Hier ist es wie im Himmel. Wenn ich nur ewig mit Dir hierbleiben koennte." ("Ach! It is like heaven here. If I could stay here forever with you.")

Hans: "Ich werde Dir's kaufen. Das hier — und die Berge dahinter!" ("I'll buy it for you. This — and all the mountains beyond!")

Frieda: "Du bist so lieb, Hans." ("You are a darling, Hans.")

The scene, which does not appear in the final cut, immediately establishes Hans and Frieda's love for each other. Viewers will remember that, in the movie, the two lovebirds are first seen at the circus, with Hans discussing his attraction to Cleopatra the trapeze artist ("She's the most beautiful big woman I've ever seen!"). What we lose is the Edenic symbolism of the garden, the innocence of the young lovers soon to be corrupted by the sinful Cleo and Hercules.

"Koo Koo! Give somebody else a chance!": Koo Koo (Minnie Woolsey) dances at the wedding feast.

Venus and Hercules

In sharp contrast to the innocence of Hans and Frieda, we are next introduced to Venus, the seal trainer. Present in the script, but absent in the movie, is a scene in which Venus is revealed to be Hercules' mistress. She enters his wagon and begins to prepare supper. When Hercules returns, he suggests farming out her favors to other men. They quarrel. Hercules is insistent:

> What harm can it do you? It can't hurt you.
> It ain't as if I'd be sore about it. Only tonight
> he was saying again he'd like to meet you.
> What easier way do you know of picking up
> a couple of hundred francs?

This brief interaction — in which we also learn that Venus has been giving Hercules money — provides Venus and Hercules with an intriguing backstory, and offers an explanation as to why they broke up. It also serves the important dramatic function of propelling Venus toward Phroso, the circus clown who becomes her new boyfriend, and eventually her protector. Moreover, it transforms our perception of Venus. In the movie, she is free-spirited, moving from one lover to the next. In the script, she comes across as a "fallen woman" attempting to reform. From this vantage point, Phroso represents her salvation from the clutches of the lecherous Hercules.

Venus and Phroso

In Venus' wagon, Venus and Phroso have a fight over Cleo's flirtations with Phroso. There is a scene, deleted from the final film, in which Venus arrives with his freshly darned socks. When he asks if she has been catching up on sleep, she replies suggestively, "Sleep isn't <u>all</u> a girl needs."

Venus later appears dressed up for a night on the town. Phroso is working on a prop bathtub. The scene is risqué, with the camera angle leading us to believe at first that he is naked, and that Venus has a clear view of his figure. They have a candid conversation in which Phroso explains his plans to settle down, marry and raise a family. Venus misunderstands, thinking he has another woman in mind, and she snaps that she is going out to find a couple of sailors. Phroso tells her to find four sailors and have a "regular time." She gets choked up with rage.

These cut scenes deepen the bond between Venus and Phroso, the "normal" couple whose affection for each other is a dramatic element that 1930s audiences would recognize. Phroso is looking forward to a future with Venus, even if she consistently misreads him. As Phroso falls more deeply in love, he becomes stronger and more possessive. When Roscoe, a stuttering clown, calls her a tramp, Phroso defends his sweetheart's honor by socking him in the mouth.

Love seems to be blooming all around the circus; even the Bearded Lady gives birth ("And it's going to have a beard!"). But it is the upcoming marriage of Hans and Cleo that causes the biggest stir.

The Wedding Feast

The wedding feast is the unforgettable centerpiece of *Freaks*, a scene that has endured in the popular imagination. Its influence can be measured by the number of cross-cultural references it has inspired, from *South Park* (1997–the present) to *The Wolf of Wall Street* (2013). The actual wedding ceremony is elided in favor of an extended sequence in which the freaks gather for a celebration that takes a sharp turn into pathos. Phroso and Venus are notably absent from this scene.

In the original script, Cleo kisses Hans, her ill-matched new husband. Hercules suggests that he will kiss the bride, too, on behalf of all the freaks. Cleo reciprocates too passionately, and Hans begins to burn with embarrassment. He attempts to stop her from drinking more wine. Frieda feels Hans' deepening shame and cannot bear it. The other freaks are caught up in the moment, blissfully ignorant of what is happening. Now it is Cleo's turn to be initiated into the fellowship of freaks. They begin their famous chant: "One of us! One of us! Gooble gobble, gooble gobble!" A fruit bowl filled with wine is passed around. By the time this "loving cup" reaches Cleo, she can no longer

The filming of the Wedding Feast scene, with Tod Browning (right) presiding.

contain her disgust and begins to scream at them. Furious, she turns on Hans:

"You spineless little runt — to sit there and let them insult your wife!"

Cleo takes aim at his dignity. Is he a man or a baby? She suggests he play horsey. Hercules is tickled by this idea and places Hans on Cleo's back. She begins to stagger around in a drunken burlesque while Hans grits his teeth.

The psychological and emotional impact of the scene is enormous. In an instant, Hans plummets from happiness to despair. Frieda, filled with empathy, is shattered by Cleo's metaphoric castration of her beloved. And the freaks, unaware of these undercurrents, consolidate into a powerful collective. Individually, they have been regarded as harmless, lovable children. But without Tetrallini to supervise their wild energy, they careen out of control.

Their willingness to accept Cleo as "one of us" is rescinded when her bigotry is revealed. This dramatic unmasking sets up the film's final and darkest act.

Tavern and Wagon

In the October 29 screenplay, but nowhere in the final film, is a scene that might explain why Venus was absent from the wedding festivities. Sitting alone in an old tavern at night, depressed over Phroso's neglect of her, she curses the proprietor: "I hope all your children will be clowns! I hope they'll all have broken hearts — and I hope they'll want a drink and no one will ever give it to 'em." When she returns to the circus, she enters Hercules' wagon and he gets her up to speed on recent events. She is disgusted: "I didn't think there was a thing in the world as low as you are. But there is — she's lower! Marrying a freak to get his money — so the both of you can wallow in it!"

Continued on page 42

CAN A FULL GROWN WOMAN TRULY LOVE A MIDGET ?

TOD BROWNING'S

PRODUCTION

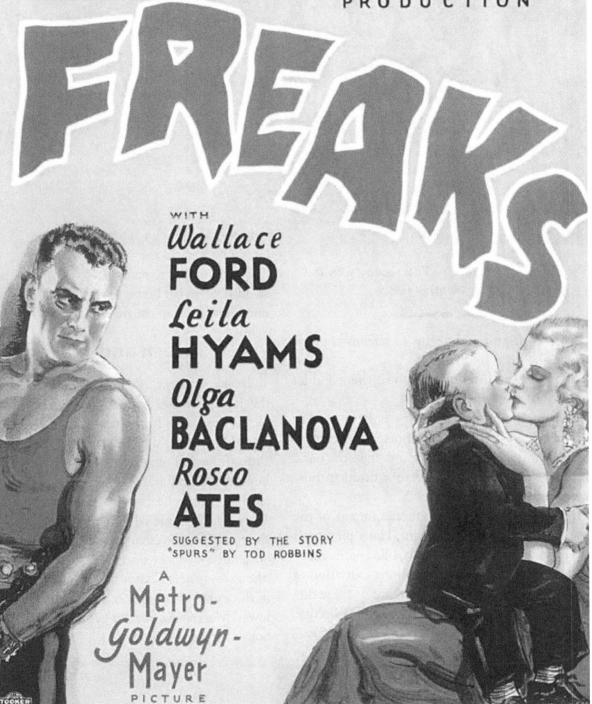

FREAKS

WITH

Wallace **FORD**

Leila **HYAMS**

Olga **BACLANOVA**

Rosco **ATES**

SUGGESTED BY THE STORY "SPURS" BY TOD ROBBINS

A Metro-Goldwyn-Mayer PICTURE

TOOKER

Browning and Baclanova in her "Duck Woman" makeup and costume.

Browning and Olga Baclanova in her "Duck Woman" makeup.

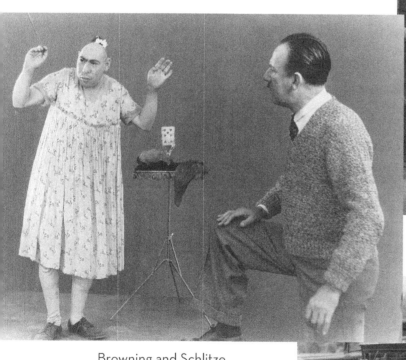

Browning (middle of back row) and the cast of *Freaks*

Browning and Schlitze.

Harry Earles, Daisy Earles, Browning and Tiny Doll.

Continued from page 39

In a shockingly violent climax, Cleo and Hercules receive their just deserts. The setting is a mountain road at night, visually reminiscent of Renfield's coach ride through the Borgo Pass in Browning's *Dracula* (1931). In this final, furious set piece, Hercules decides to kill Venus. Phroso defends her. Simultaneously, the freaks confront Cleo, who takes flight through the rain-soaked forest. The freaks give chase and do something indescribably terrible to her. In Browning's capable hands, this sequence is splendidly atmospheric and genuinely spooky.

The original screenplay is even more complex and explicit.

Circus Wagon on Mountain Road at Night

Of all the scenes that were filmed but then trimmed from the final version of *Freaks*, this is the one most sought after by movie buffs. The explosion of pure horror described here could explain why the preview audience stampeded out of the theater. Some highlights include:

- 💀 Hercules climbs into the seat of Venus' wagon, offers the driver a drink, and chokes him to death.

- 💀 A heavy wagon crushes Hercules' leg.

- 💀 Venus protects Frieda in her arms, but attracts the attention of Hercules, who clutches at her skirt.

- 💀 Cleo runs along the road, looking back in horror over her shoulder. A bolt of lightning strikes a tree. She sees it falling — but too late. She disappears under the heavy branches of the tree as it strikes the ground. The freaks run in and swarm over the tree after her. We cannot see what they are doing, but we can hear her ungodly screams.

- 💀 Hercules drags himself to the wagon door and pulls himself inside, but as he tries to

"Cain't a Roman lady it-it-itch?": Roscoe (Roscoe Ates) and Hercules (Henry Victor) discuss a circus routine.

close the door, the monstrosities rush into the scene. They throw things at the door, which gives way, and they pour into the wagon.

The film's equally infamous coda, which contains the shock image of what remains of Cleo after the freaks have had their way with her, is emblazoned in the memories of everyone who has seen it. However, the 62-minute version leaves important questions dangling. Do Venus and Phroso become a couple? Did Hercules survive? The original screenplay ties up these loose ends.

Tetrallini's Freaks and Music Hall

Phroso and Venus, visiting their old friend Madame Tetrallini, show her a photo of Hans and Frieda with their baby. The picture is signed: "To

Phroso and Venus, with love, from Hans and Frieda." We learn that the two little people were married three years ago in Australia. Tetrallini explains that her "children" are working through the winter.

VENUS: I see you've got the old bunch with you.

TETRALLINI: Yes — and Cleo is with me too.

PHROSO: Cleo? Oh, yes, in a music hall.

TETRALLINI: No, in the first pit over there.

VENUS: In a pit?

TETRALLINI: Yes, she's working as a freak now.

Tetrallini leads the way to a pit, from which the sound of a duck quacking can be heard. And there is Cleo, horribly mutilated, dressed as a duck woman. Her legs are gone, one eye is gone, her nose is broken, scars are on her face. At intervals, she utters the imbecilic cry: "QUACK QUACK!"

Venus calls out to her. At the sound of her name, she looks up. For a moment, there seems to be a glimmer of intelligence, of recognition in her eye, but this passes at once.

TETRALLINI: "I guess it's best she can't remember."

Shooting over two or three rows of heads, we see a small stage before which an orchestra of three or four pieces is gathered. A bum xylophone and puppeteering act is just finishing. The crowd applauds — they take their bow and exit.

Hercules walks on the stage and the camera moves up to a medium shot of Hercules, who is a little fat now, and dressed in a tuxedo. The orchestra starts "The Rosary" and all else grows quiet.

Hercules begins to sing in a beautiful tenor

voice: "The hours I spent with thee, dear heart," etc. etc.

And from the pit off scene, comes the harsh sound of Cleo's voice: "QUACK QUACK!"

FADE OUT

The Preview (January, 1932)

Production stills confirm that much of what has been described above was indeed filmed once *Freaks* went into production in November 1931. A cut running approximately 90 minutes was tested in front of a Southern California audience in early January 1932. While notes from this screening are unavailable, Browning biographers David J. Skal and Elias Savada claim that it was met with strong negative reactions. One woman apparently attempted to sue MGM on the grounds that the movie precipitated a miscarriage.

Following the disastrous preview, Thalberg ordered that a "happy ending" be filmed with Hans and Frieda reuniting. Browning spent four days in reshoots, and an intense editing session followed. (In the classical studio era, directors rarely had "final cut" privileges.)

Dialogue Cutting Continuity Scripts (January 29, 1932, and February 11, 1932)

These revised scripts were prepared for editor Basil Wrangell after the preview screening and contain dialogue as well as information about camera angles and movement. Since the modified complete script is unavailable, these documents provide valuable information about the material added during reshoots. The new footage included:

 The wraparound story of a spieler in a sideshow boasting of living, breathing monstrosities: "Offend one and you offend them all!"

 A new scene at the circus with Hans admiring Cleo during her high-wire act. Frieda teases him:

"The Bearded Lady's baby is born!": Phroso (Wallace Ford), Stork Woman (Elizabeth Green) and Half-Boy (Johnny Eck) spread the glad tidings.

"Hook up our dress": Roscoe (Roscoe Ates) attends to his wife Daisy (Daisy Hilton--right) and her sister Violet (Violet Hilton--left).

HANS

She's the most beautiful big woman I've ever seen.

FRIEDA

Why Hans, how you talk! I should be pretty jealous soon.

A moment of comedy between one of the Rollo brothers — an acrobat — and the Living Torso:

ROLLO BROTHER: Well, catch our act tomorrow night. We got something new.

THE LIVING TORSO: Can you do something with your eyebrow?

A moment of risqué humor between Cleo and Hercules:

CLEO (preparing eggs)
How do you like them?

HERCULES (looking at her breasts)
Not bad.

The addition of an intertitle, as in a silent movie:

The revelation that Hercules was castrated is replaced by an off-screen death. The footage of the freaks swarming Cleo, pinned under the fallen branch, was deleted. Another casualty was the character of Madame Tetrallini. Originally, the freaks' handler was to have had more screen time, swimming, drinking, ordering them to bed, mobilizing men to help quench a fire during the climactic wagon scene and, of course, greeting Venus and Phroso at her dime museum. Now that these moments no longer exist, she barely registers as a character.

The Theatrical Release

Freaks was released in Los Angeles on February 12, 1932, before rolling out to the rest of the country. It failed to recoup its $316,000 budget. On August 7, MGM pulled it from distribution. It represented a net loss of $164,000. Thalberg attempted to reissue the film in 1933 as *Nature's Mistakes*, and may have been responsible for adding the prologue commonly attributed to Dwain Esper:

Before proceeding with the showing of the following

HIGHLY

UNUSUAL ATTRACTION,

a few words should be said about the amazing subject matter.

BELIEVE IT OR NOT ----

STRANGE AS IT SEEMS.

In ancient times anything that deviated from the normal was considered an omen of ill luck or representative of evil. Gods of misfortune and adversity were invariably cast in the form of monstrosities, and deeds of injustice and hardship have been attributed to the many crippled and deformed tyrants of Europe and Asia.

HISTORY, RELIGION,

FOLKLORE and **LITERATURE**

abound in tales of misshapen misfits who have altered the world's course. **GOLIATH, CALIBAN, FRANKENSTEIN, GLOUCESTER, TOM THUMB,** and **KAISER WILHELM** are just a few, whose fame is world wide.

The accident of abnormal birth was considered a disgrace and malformed children were placed out in the elements to die. If, perchance, one of these freaks of nature survived, he was always regarded with suspicion. Society shunned him because of his deformity, and a family so hampered was always ashamed of the curse put upon it.

Occasionally, one of these unfortunates was taken to court to be jeered at or ridiculed for the amusement of the nobles. Others were left to eke out a living by begging, stealing or starving.

For the love of beauty is a deep seated urge which dates back to the beginning of civilization. The revulsion with which we view the abnormal, the malformed and the mutilated is the result of long conditioning by our forefathers. The majority of freaks, themselves, are endowed with normal thoughts and emotions. Their lot is truly a heart-breaking one.

They are forced into the most unnatural of lives. Therefore, they have built up among themselves a code of ethics to protect them from the barbs of normal people.

Their rules are rigidly adhered to and the hurt of one is the hurt of all; the joy of one is the joy of all. The story about to be revealed is a story based on the effect of this code upon their lives.

Never again will such a story be filmed, as modern science and teratology is rapidly eliminating such blunders of nature from the world.

With humility for the many injustices done to such people, (they have no power to control their lot) we present the most startling horror story of the **ABNORMAL** and **THE UNWANTED**.

The Dwain Esper Reissue

In 1948, Dwain Esper, director of the exploitation classic *Maniac* (1934), bought *Freaks* from MGM for $50,000 and took it on the road, exhibiting it under the titles *Nature's Mistakes*, *The Monster Show* and *Forbidden Love*. He retained the rights for 25 years. Viewers who experienced the film in the 1950s and '60s most likely saw this version, which did not include the happy ending with Hans and Frieda.

Even in its compromised form, *Freaks* slowly garnered a cult following in Europe, and re-emerged during the 1962 Cannes Festival Repertory. The changing attitude toward people with disabilities, as well as the evolution of the word "freak" from a pejorative to a complimentary term, no doubt contributed to its reappraisal.

Turner and Warner Bros. Home Video

In 1986, Turner Entertainment acquired MGM's pre–1986 film library. Warner Home Video distributed *Freaks* on DVD in 2003, with its happy ending intact. The present writer's introduction to *Freaks* came in the late 1990s via Turner Classic Movies, which has made it a popular favorite around Halloween.

Conclusion

The circuitous journey of *Freaks* reached an elegant conclusion of sorts in 2020, when Tartarus Press published a handsome collection of Tod Robbins short stories under the title *Unholy Tales*. The volume contains several of the author's most memorable creations, including "Spurs." The dust jacket features the original poster art for *Freaks*. And so we come full circle, from print to screen to print again. Perhaps one day the complete original screenplay will also be published so that fans can read it for themselves. Although the "Browning version" of this extraordinary film is lost to history, the documents that survive provide a tantalizing reconstruction of an even more potent masterwork.

Mark of the Vampires of Prague

by Gary D. Rhodes

"Ancient horrors of the distant past." Those words are spoken by Prof. Zelen, not on-screen as portrayed by Lionel Barrymore in *Mark of the Vampire* (1935), but in one of a number of script drafts that reveal the story's evolution.

At least five different versions of the script survive, all archived at the Margaret Herrick Library and all bearing the title *The Vampires of Prague*: a September 26, 1934, draft by Guy Endore (which also features a handwritten date of October 1, 1934), an October 5, 1934 draft "dictated by Guy Endore, Bernard Schubert, Tod Browning"; a November 1, 1934, draft with the by-line "B. Schubert" and "G. Endore," a December 20, 1934, draft (which also features two handwritten dates, December 26 and December 27), with the byline "Guy Endore [and] Bernard Schubert" plus "Additional Dialogue: Messrs. Ornitz & Kraft"; and a January 8, 1935, draft that features "Dialogue Changes" by John L. Balderston.

The bloodthirsty Count Mora (Bela Lugosi) and his daughter Luna (Carroll Borland) make the abandoned Borotyn Castle their neck of the woods in *Mark of the Vampire*.

How many scripts were there? The answer is unknown, but communications between MGM and the Production Code Administration refer to a draft dated November 12, 1934. That suggests that at least six different scripts were written, possibly more. For years, film historians have speculated in print and on audio commentaries about changes made to the scripts and the completed film, but none have closely examined these surviving materials. This makes much of what has been claimed in the past spurious.

Mark of the Vampire remains best remembered for being a remake of Browning's lost film *London After Midnight* (1927), including its closing revelation that the on-screen vampires are fakes. However, such a limited view does not take into account how much *Mark of the Vampire* also drew upon Browning's *Dracula* (1931), as well as the extent to which its story evolved, incorporating the old while inventing the new. Its ancient horrors deserve rediscovery, including those buried in the distant past of script drafts that were never filmed.

The Film's Opening

Surviving scripts indicate that the barely remembered Midwife character (played by Jessie Ralph) was intended to have a much larger role. The September 26, 1934, draft begins as follows:

> We open in a graveyard at the fall of day. Behind dull purple clouds that are scurrying across a gray autumn sky the sun is beginning to set. A cold evening wind arises and sweeps the last dry leaves from the bare trees and hustles them down the rows of tottering tombstones, where lie forgotten ancestors of the little village of Visoka, some forty miles from Prague.
>
> Marjanna Zleniska, the village midwife and herb doctor, an ancient witch-like crone, has lingered in her passage through the graveyard, and now attracted by a bunch of rare herbs sprouting beside a tombstone she sets down a bundle of weeds from her back and stoops, and with her heavy thumb she begins to burrow among the precious medicinal roots. But suddenly she becomes aware of the sun fast slipping below the hilly horizon. She stops, frightened, and looks around. An evening mist is creeping up along the ground. The wind tears the mist into ragged wraiths.
>
> The midwife hesitates, still stooped over her task but no longer grubbing among the herbs. The moan of the wind and fading daylight sap her courage. And suddenly a bat flits by, weaving its mysterious way among the tombstones. That unnerves Marjanna. She drops herbs and swinging her bundle on her back dashes off madly.
>
> But an iron cross, rusted and bent, fallen from some neglected tomb and lying hidden in the long grass catches her skirt. She stops dead, not daring to look around to face whatever evil power has caught hold of her.

She is paralyzed with fear, and can do nothing but cross and cross herself again, and mutter prayers.

> The skirt tears and she is released. Hardly daring to believe her good fortune she dashes on again, and, her eyes agog with fear and her wispy [gray] hair streaming from her kerchief that has slipped from her head she goes racing past the camera.

The script then calls for a dissolve to a "crazy old hut, tumbledown and weather-beaten, thatched and overgrown with thorny vines. A sick fence reels around it. A cracked sign reads: Parodni Baba, which translated reads Midwife. Into the hut the old witch runs, pauses at the door, startled at the sight of smoke rising from a kettle at the hearth." The script indicates that she sells wolf's claw and white thorn "as protection against the evil that comes by night."

Inside the hut, the Midwife finds her albino daughter, Fidelja, who has left a boiling brew meant to cure a farmer's cow. A third resident is a black cat, one that

> rises from its sleep and arches its back. Its fur bristles. The cat spits. The old witch pauses with her broom upraised, and follows the direction of the cat's poised body. At the darkling window a bat is fluttering. It backs away and comes forward again, knocking itself against the pane, as if seeking to enter.

The Midwife cries out, "A vampire! Heaven help us!" She instructs Fidelja, "Fetch me that wreath of wolf's claw. Quick! Of all nights to be caught unprotected. Walpurgis night when evil is abroad [more] than on all the rest of the nights of the year together."

The October 5, 1934, script retains the basics of these events while using more atmospheric language. For example, it mentions a rising mist, "as though the graves are giving up the dead." It also presents a revised description of how the Midwife's skirt tears. It gets caught on "what seems to be a skeleton's hand reaching up out of the ground," but is in fact a gardener's tool. The Midwife remains in the November 1 draft, with new dialogue that calls Walpurgis Night the time "when all the fiends of

The aggressive Police Inspector Neumann (Lionel Atwill) orders Dr. Doskil (Donald Meek) to determine the cause of Sir Karell's death.

hell are loose!" She also appears in the December 20 draft.

Whether any of this action appeared in the January 8, 1935, script is unknown: Its first several pages are missing. And the Midwife hardly appears in the completed film. She gathers bat thorn in the cemetery until a bat scares her. She runs away until her skirt becomes caught on a gardener's tool that does indeed look like a skeleton's hand. Were any of her other actions filmed? It is difficult to say, but the fact that she is the eighth actor listed in the on-screen credits — above seven others who have dialogue in the final film — suggests the answer is probably yes.

Fedor Attacked

In the September 26, 1934, draft, the character we know in the movie as Fedor (played by Henry Wadsworth) is named Teodor Vincenty. Before any vampires appear on-screen, he leaves the baron's home and walks across the "neglected" Borotyn estate at night.

As he rushes thru [*sic*] the dark woods he hears a curious crackling noise and stops, frightened in spite of himself, but hearing again the whistle of the train he races on when suddenly his foot catches in something and he takes a bad fall and lies on the ground unconscious. He is just in front of the tunnel-like archway that is the entrance to the Borotyn Castle. And it seems as if from the shadows of that archway something that is a shadow itself, detaches itself

Director Browning and cinematographer James Wong Howe have front row seats as Lugosi and Borland go into their undead act.

and moves towards the young man, swoops down upon him and blankets him in its darkness, and then the shadow moves back toward the archway, dragging its unconscious prey along the ground. FADE OUT.

Teodor returns to the baron's home, his hair mussed, his forehead swelling, and his shirt open at the neck.

In the October 5, 1934, draft, Teodor becomes Fedor. He trips and is dragged away just as he was in the prior script. The same is true in the scripts of November 1 and December 20. But in the completed film, the action is not seen. Fedor arrives at Baron von Zinden's home and briefly recounts fall-

ing down by the Borotyn Castle. He has wounds on his neck, which causes the maid Annie (June Gittelson) to scream about vampires. It is possible the vampire attack on him was filmed and later cut.

The Vampires Appear

Count Mora and Luna did not have names until the December 20, 1934, script. The third vampire — seated by Count Mora while Luna flies down to the castle floor on bat wings — never received a character name, even though he has dialogue in the final scene of the completed film.

The September 26, 1934, script introduces the vampires as follows:

FADE IN - The last rays of the sun have lit up for a moment the broken panes of the old tower that houses the circular staircase of the Borotyn Castle. The camera approaches one cobwebby window from which a bat is seen to escape and flit out into the gathering night. A faint glow illuminates the window. It is the light of a candle, and as we come nearer we see two mysterious figures, bearing lighted tapers, moving slowly past us down the stairs.

WE DISSOLVE TO:

A long shot of a vast hall where the sheeted tables and chairs are like ghosts. Old armor stands rigidly before the dusty panelled walls. Down the stairs glide the two figures and move toward a door. From room to room they go as if they were looking for some one [*sic*]. Rats scurry along the corners of the floor. Spiders run to the centers of their vast nets. A procession of strange bugs in army-like formation moves across the floor intent upon some obscure business of [their] own.

The two figures enter a dark crypt. The heavy stone pilasters are wet with the sweat of the underground, the ponderous vaults drip water from their sparkling stalactites, and all this takes on a formidable character in the vague flickering light of the candles as the two figures enter. One of them points. Yes, that's it. They have found what they were looking for, a long box-like a [*sic*] coffin and lying thereon a man, dressed in evening dress. A man of pallid countenance, sleeping a strange sleep, who slowly rises to sitting position.

Maria (Leila Bennett), the baron's maid, and the Groom (Franklyn Ardell, whose character was later renamed "Chauffeur") race through the night in a carriage. The script explains:

They are just passing the old castle where mysterious lights are seen passing the windows. The groom begins at once to cross himself. "My God, it's the vampires!" he yells.

Maria screams too. Both look toward the castle as if hypnotized. And they see with horror-stricken eyes the great portal swing open slowly and a shrouded woman ap-

pears in the opening. Maria shrieks and clasps the groom in a death-grip. He pushes her aside and whips up the horse and away they tear. The camera remains behind for a brief glimpse of the mysterious woman who slowly issues from the castle.

The October 5, 1934, draft — on which Browning worked — provides the following elaborate description:

The two figures descending the steps are clothed in burial garb, as if they had just stepped out of their coffins, the woman's soft gray shroud trailing behind her. We hear the sound of scurrying claws and feet as though everything with life and blood is fleeing from them to safety. They hesitate and look over the railing. Three armadillos dash for their [lives] and burrow under an old piece of furniture. A fat spider, whose web stretches from a piece of old armor to a dusty window, races across his web and buries himself in a crack in the wall. The man and woman note these things with unchanged expressions. Their attention is finally attracted by a swishing sound of wings flapping above them. They glance up to see a bat just dropping from the eaves. Another bat now comes to life, leaves the molding and joins the first, and the two float over toward the man and woman, as though to accompany them down the stairs.

They continue on down the stairs and enter an arched doorway into a gloomy room. They seem to glide through giant spider webs without breaking a single strand and look about as though bent on some mysterious quest. The vast army of crawling life that infests the floor and walls scatters madly seeking shelter.

Here are clear influences from Browning's *Dracula*, including the plan to use armadillos. And the descriptions indicate a point that may not otherwise be clear in viewing the film, a point that might also shed light on a similar scene in *Dracula*. Rather than simply being fellow creatures of the night, the animals and insects are literally fleeing

Jean Hersholt and Elizabeth Allan.

from the vampires. This explains Browning's use of a fake spider in both films, whereas the other animals and insects are real: He needed the spiders to move as rapidly as possible.

The November 1 draft offers yet another fascinating variation on the vampires' first appearance:

FADE IN

CLOSEUP —

of a section of a window in the tower of the castle — the panes broken and dusty and thick with cob webs [*sic*]. The last rays of the sun light it up for a moment — then the light fades out. A bat starts to wiggle its way through the broken glass as the CAMERA TRUCKS BACK to a MEDIUM SHOT

— the bat finally works its way through the broken window and escapes into the night.

From within the castle is HEARD a weird howl like a wolf — as though coming from the bowels of the castle. Faint candle-light glows from the inside and through rifts in the tattered curtain, two corpse-like figures, a man and a woman, are seen — the man carrying a heavy candle — they pass, in deathlike silence.

LONG SHOT - INT. MAIN HALL OF CASTLE

The vast, gloomy interior — chairs and tables covered with sheets, like so many silent ghosts — a massive staircase, the steps of which are covered with dust, leads into the darkness above. Old armor stands rigidly before the stone walls, where hang ancient tapestries. In every corner spiders have stretched their gray webs. Through the broken windows, where remnants of once splendid curtains now hang in dirty rags, the moonlight filters down upon this scene of ruin and decay.

Descending the stairs are the two corpse-like creatures.

The November 1 script describes Luna's appearance outside the castle in greater detail than before:

Approaching CAMERA SHOT — as seen from [the maid] Maria's angle — the great ornamental rusty gates of iron scrolls attached to great stone pillars, against which leans a dead tree. Behind the gates, enveloped in a ghostly mist, stands the corpse-like woman — her burning eyes illuminating her death-like face, as she gazes fixedly at the approaching rig.

The script calls for a medium shot of the castle gate in which "[t]he corpse-like woman gazes after the departing rig — then turns and glides back into the castle grounds — the mist seems to cling to her and follow with her."

On-screen, the vampires' first appearance unfolds much as it was planned, with more moving camera than any of the scripts suggested.

Luna Attacks

In the September 26, 1934, draft, the particular vampire that tries to molest Irena (Elizabeth Allan) is unnamed, and possibly not even female:

A long shot of the terrace bathed in moonlight where the mist is still low. The bat that we had seen flitting about before is no longer a bat. It is bat-like, large and black and with wings like a bat or perhaps that is only a wide black cloak, for the creature that wears it is no longer flying, but walking, or rather gliding along the grass, its feet bathed in the mist. And it advances toward the terrace where Irena is sitting.

Irena sees it coming toward her, and she is startled, but she makes no move. Her eyes

are wide open and set and thus she remains, awaiting the creature's approach.

The creature comes up to the terrace, climbs the steps and walks up to Irena who still makes no move.

"Good evening," says Irena as if she were talking in her sleep.

The creature says nothing and remains standing there by Irena's   chair.

"Won't you sit down[?]" Irena urges in an even voice.

And still the creature says nothing, but only looks at Irena.

"Strange," says Irena, "how…drowsy…I feel…Forgive me…But I

feel…so…strange."

And still the creature says nothing, but when Irena's head droops, it bends over the girl and enfolds [her] in that cloak that is like the wings of a bat.

In the October 5, 1934, draft, Irena describes for Prof. Zelen a memory of a female vampire, one that was likely not intended to appear on-screen:

I was seated on the terrace in the moonlight when I saw what first appeared to be a mist moving across the lawn toward me — a mist which seemed to melt away and transform itself into a pale, beautiful woman in flowing robes, who continued to approach. I arose from my chair and bid her good evening, but received no answer. She continued to come closer until she stood right in front of me. I tried to speak to her again but her eyes — her eyes were blazing — they held me entranced and robbed me of my power of speech. I felt faint and fell back into my chair, limp and drowsy. My eyes slowly closed — I was powerless to open them. Even though I could not see, I knew she was approaching. Suddenly she tore the scarf from my neck — then I felt her breath upon my throat — it was deathly cold, at

In a posed shot, Lugosi (with bullet wound makeup) terrorizes his co-stars Elizabeth Allan and Henry Wadsworth.

first — and then — then — a sweet stinging pain passed through my entire body — and I knew no more.

The completed film depicts Luna slowly approaching Irena on the terrace and seemingly biting her on the neck. Maria the maid discovers her limp body. Later, Irena recounts the event to Prof. Zelen, but in the space of only three sentences.

The January 8, 1935, script contains the following brief scene, one which does appear in the completed film:

LONG SHOT - ELEVATED - CASTLE GROUNDS

as seen from Irena's view. Under the moonlight in the castle grounds, is an old tree. A light mist is floating by. In the shadow of the tree stands Luna — her burning eyes staring fixedly up toward Irena's balcony.

By contrast, the scene in which Luna hisses at Fedor as he interrupts her effort to bite Irena does not appear in any of the surviving scripts.

Count Mora Attacks

In the September 26, 1934, draft, Maria details the vampire's invasion of the baron's home as a flashback depicted on-screen:

She leaves Miss Borotyn in the bedroom and goes into the sitting room. A dark shape hovers before one window [, finds] a wreath of wolf's claw there, shields the sight of

Bela Lugosi, Carroll Borland, Elizabeth Allan and Henry Wadsworth in another posed shot.

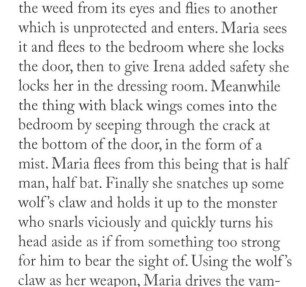

Behind the scenes on *Mark of the Vampire*.

the weed from its eyes and flies to another which is unprotected and enters. Maria sees it and flees to the bedroom where she locks the door, then to give Irena added safety she locks her in the dressing room. Meanwhile the thing with black wings comes into the bedroom by seeping through the crack at the bottom of the door, in the form of a mist. Maria flees from this being that is half man, half bat. Finally she snatches up some wolf's claw and holds it up to the monster who snarls viciously and quickly turns his head aside as if from something too strong for him to bear the sight of. Using the wolf's claw as her weapon, Maria drives the vampire from the room out of the window.

In the October 5 draft, Maria also recounts the vampire attack in the form of a flashback, its action depicted visually:

DISSOLVE to Old Jan [portrayed by actor Ivan Simpson] locking the door. Fearfully, he turns to Maria and asks what has happened. Maria exclaims, "A vampire! A vampire!" Then, to their consternation, a mist comes seeping through a crack beneath the door, rises like a cloud, then takes the form of a corpse-like man. He stares at Jan and Maria — his eyes seem to burn through them — as they back away from him in fear, he glides toward the closet where Irena is hiding. Jan becomes panicky — he sees the wolf's-claw lying on the bed — nudges Maria and points toward it. She snatches up the weed, runs to the vampire, pushes it toward his face — he turns on her and snarls like a vicious wolf. She pokes it at him again. Then, swishing his cape like a pair of wings...

The script notes a dissolve back to Maria, who concludes with the dialogue, "with his cape spread like giant black wings, he flew out of the window!" The November 1 draft suggests a medium shot of French doors

> leading out onto the balcony at the end of the hall. The doors are open. A large bat is fluttering outside — a halo of mist about it, through which its eyes burn and its sharp white teeth gleam. The mist surrounding the bat grows so dense as to obscure the bat. The mist moves forward through the door and into the hall — takes on an elongated form until it trails on the floor. A pair of burning eyes appear[s] through the mist — then a white face — until at last the mist becomes the cloak of the corpse-like man of the castle. He glides silently toward Jan and Maria.

The January 8, 1935, script repeated the same basic description. While the completed film does not show Count Mora's eyes before showing his face, it does offer similar action presented as a flashback, introduced not by Maria but by Jan.

Luna Takes Flight

In the September 26, 1934, draft, Luna's then-unnamed vampire does not fly, but the continuity makes clear the purpose of the vampire gathering. Prof. Zelen and the baron clearly see the activity through the castle window. The events have been arranged specifically to frighten the baron. By the time of the October 5 draft, the scene had changed notably:

> The great music [room] of the castle is illuminated by the pale moonlight streaming through broken windows, assisted by the wavering flames of two massive candles. A thick layer of dust blankets the floor and lies heavy on the sheeted furniture. Spiders unhindered have stretched their great cobwebs from every projection. Rusted suits of armor stand before the walls where hang faded, weather-beaten tapestries. At the far end of the room, towering to the beamed ceiling, are dust-covered organ pipes which in the

flickering light of the candles appear like ghostly sentinels on guard.

> Before the great fireplace, cheerless and cold without its fire, are two corpse-like figures in burial garb, stiffly seated as if in silent council, the only life in their dead and wax-like faces the blaze of their burning eyes.

> From the organ console, spiders have built giant webs up to a lofty window, through whose broken, cobwebby panes the moonlight filters down upon another corpse-like figure whom we have never seen before. Corpse-like fingers wander softly over the keyboard evoking a funereal dirge that is like the moaning of tortured souls.

> One of the figures at the fireplace slowly turns his gaze up to the ceiling where a giant bat, hanging head downward from a beam, comes out of its torpor, releases itself and flapping its tremendous wings slowly starts to encircle the room.

The November 1 draft features the same basic description, notably adding the following:

MED. SHOT - BEFORE FIREPLACE

One of the two corpse-like figures seated before the fireplace slowly turns his gaze up to the ceiling.

SEMI CLOSE SHOT -

of a beam at the ceiling. A giant bat, hanging head downward from the beam, comes out of its torpor, rears itself, and flapping its tremendous

wings, slowly flies away.

MED. SHOT - CORPSE AT CONSOLE OF ORGAN

still playing softly. The bat, now its former size, slowly floats into scene, circling over the organist's head.

LONG SHOT - INT. MUSIC ROOM - ELEVATED SHOT

as if seen from window. The room is the same as before, except that the bat is now a terrifying creature — half-woman and

812·32

MGM dropped the title *The Vampires of Prague* in response to a complaint from — Prague. The Czech city felt that tourists would get the idea that it was infested with vampires and, according to *Variety* (December 24, 1935), were prepared to take the matter up with the League of Nations(!). To avoid a hold-up in the movie's foreign release, Metro made the switch to *Mark of the Vampire*.

To indicate clearly that the scene is a show staged to scare the baron, the script suggests that he and Zelen look through the window after the medium shot of the "Corpse at Console of Organ." The baron and Zelen appear again at the end of this scene, "their terror-stricken faces ashen white in the moonlight." It is also evident that the two men witness Luna's flight in the December 20, 1934, script.

The Film's Conclusion

The September 26, 1934, draft ends with two brief but very important concluding scenes:

> The hall... The female vampire and the other vampires are taking off their makeup and their clothes and have their trunks, etc. out. On the trunks is printed "Luna and Company — Flying Acrobats." One of the vampires is saying to Luna: "Well, that's a job I don't care to go through again… All this vampire business nearly drove me mad." Luna: "Oh, stop kicking! You got more in the last few nights than you could get in a month doing three a day!"

The scene cuts to Irena, Teodor (Fedor), Maria and the police inspector (played on-screen by Lionel Atwill). Teodor indicates that he wasn't in on the scheme.

The November 1 script unfolds with a number of small but quite notable differences:

LONG SHOT - INT. RECEPTION ROOM OF CASTLE

In the f.g. is a big wicker traveling case, plainly lettered:

> LUNA
> The
> BAT WOMAN
> Theatre

Luna and the un-dead creatures, their

Lionel Barrymore as Prof. Von Zelen - *Dracula's Van Helsing* in everything but name.

half-bat — burning eyes illuminating the death-like face. With her bat-like wings, she flies past the organ and swoops down over the head of the corpse at the organ and with lazy strokes flies forward and alights on the floor beside the two figures before the fireplace. She folds her wings closely to her side, becoming part of her shroud-like garment. The music stops. The corpse at the console turns in his seat — slowly rises — and starts forward to join the group. There is a death-like silence in the room — not even the sound of his footfalls.

Prof. Zelen scrutinizes Irena's throat for the ... Mark of the Vampire.

ghostly makeup now removed, are packing ropes and other paraphernalia used in their act. One of the two men complains and grumbles as he slams things into the basket.

Immediately thereafter, there is the final scene:

IRENA

Fedor — it's been like a horrible nightmare. If only I could have told you! But they wouldn't let me. They were afraid you would prevent me from going through with it.

FEDOR (consoling her)

It's all over now, darling. You must try and forget it.

In this version, Maria and the inspector do not appear in the scene.

The December 20 draft made further alterations to the concluding scenes, including with the vampire actors:

LONG SHOT — INT. RECEPTION ROOM - CASTLE

In the f.g. is a big wicker traveling case, plainly lettered:

> LUNA
> THE
> BAT WOMAN
> Theatre

Luna is removing her ghostly makeup, before a mirror. One of the "un-dead creatures" is packing ropes and other paraphernalia used in their act. Count Mora, still in his makeup, stands by, silently gazing over Luna's shoulder into the mirror.

COUNT MORA (proudly)

This vampire business — it's given me a

great idea for a new act. Luna — in the new act, I will be a vampire. Did you watch me? I gave all of me! I was greater than any <u>real</u> vampire!

LUNA

Sure — sure! But get off your makeup.

THE OTHER VAMPIRE

Yes — and help me with some of this packing!

This draft ends with Irena shuddering and going into Fedor'ss arms. She says that they didn't tell him about the scheme because they knew he wouldn't let her go through with it. Irena then announces that she wants to go away. "Yes, dear," he replies, without kissing her. She adds, "Far away!"

By January 8, 1935, the film's ending had changed again, eliminating the final scene with Irena and Fedor and giving new dialogue to Count Mora and Luna:

MED. SHOT - INT. RECEPTION
ROOM - CASTLE

In the f.g. is a big wicker traveling case, plainly lettered:

LUNA
THE
BAT WOMAN

Luna is removing her ghostly makeup before a mirror. One of the "dead-alive" creatures is packing ropes and other paraphernalia used in their act. Count Mora, still in his makeup, stands by, silently gazing over Luna's shoulder into the mirror.

CLOSE - MORA

COUNT MORA (proudly)

I gave all of me. I was greater than any <u>real</u> vampire! And it's given me an inspiration for a new act — I shall play a vampire — I shall turn into a bat!

TWO SHOT - MORA AND LUNA

LUNA

Aw, get off your makeup — forget vampires — you can't sell that stuff to an audience

— they'd never believe in it. Say, who d'yuh think you are? Dracula?

Roll End Credits

The completed film did not include the reference to Dracula; the final scene reverted back to the December 20, 1934, version. For that matter, some aspects of the story that seemed overly similar to Browning's *Dracula* were also changed. The herb "wolf's claw" became "bat thorn," perhaps because the former sounded too close to "wolf's bane." References to Walpurgis Night were deleted, and no armadillos appeared on-screen. The January 8, 1935, script even has Zelen using the term "dead-alive" as opposed to "undead," the former being a term he does use in the completed film. This is all in addition to changing the method of a vampire's destruction so as to be different from *Dracula*. The September 26, 1934, script has the professor explain that their heads must be severed, and wolf's claw placed in the wound; his same basic description (the herb updated to "bat thorn") appears in the completed film.

Along with insulating the film from charges of copyright infringement, the evolution from script to screen also tempered the film's gruesomeness. The September 26 script called for a close-up of the "dead man's neck, on which we see two red dots, similar to but larger than those a snake would cause." Then the December 20, 1934, and January 8, 1935, scripts featured a description of a great closeup of "PROFESSOR AND BAT":

The Professor's face comes still closer — until he is almost touching the bat. He stops. The silence in the room is unbearable. Into the scene comes the Professor's hand, holding a magnifying glass, which he places between his eyes and the face of the bat.

INSERT - MAGNIFYING GLASS

behind which, magnified, are seen the terrifying eyes and face of the bat.

None of these images are found in the film.

Concerning Horror Films.

To the Screen Editor:

There is a good deal of criticism of obscene and vulgar movies. Many of them are bad enough. But a dozen of the worst obscene pictures cannot equal the damage that is done by such films as "The Mark of the Vampire."

I do not refer to the utter sense-lessness of the picture. I do not even refer to its effect in spreading and fostering the most obnoxious superstitions. I refer to the terrible effect that it has on the only unstable but even normal men, women and children.

I am not speaking in the abstract; I am basing myself upon facts. Several people have come to my notice who, after seeing that horrible picture, suffered a nervous shock, were attacked with insomnia, and those who did fall asleep were tortured by most horrible nightmares.

In my opinion, it is a crime to produce and to present such films. We must guard not only our people's morals—we must be as careful of their physical and mental health.

WILLIAM J. ROBINSON, M. D.
New York City.

A letter published in *The New York Times* on July 28, 1935.

According to horror film mythology, *Mark of the Vampire*'s key change from script to screen came not in any of the aforementioned topics, but rather the explanation of how Count Mora and Luna became vampires. Allegedly, one or more scripts suggested incest, meaning that Mora slept with his daughter Luna and then committed suicide by shooting himself in the head. Despite being cut narratively (or even cinematically, for those who believe such story material was filmed), a trace of the suicide is visible on-screen: Lugosi's makeup as Count Mora notably features what appears to be a bullet wound near his right temple.

But none of these story details appears in the scripts of September 26, October 5 or November 1. The December 20 draft's only reference to the suicide is in a description, not in any character dialogue or on-screen action that an audience would have heard or seen:

> On Count Mora's forehead is plainly visible the frightful self-inflicted wound by which he brought his life to an end. Luna, her pale beauty unmarred by the ravages of death, walks beside him — her soft gray shroud trailing behind her.

When Count Mora invades the baron's home, the December 20 script notes: "A pair of burning eyes appear through the mist — then a white face, with a ghastly scar on the temple. The mist clears and Count Mora glides silently toward Jan and Maria." Later, Maria tells the inspector and the professor, "He had a white face — a dead white face — with burning eyes — and a ghastly wound on his forehead!" In the completed film, Maria does speak this dialogue, though she says "head" instead of "forehead."

Importantly, no surviving script mentions or implies incest. Perhaps another script draft did, but that seems very unlikely. At the time, the Production Code Administration discouraged suicide as a plot element, and the Motion Picture Production Code strictly forbade "sex perversion or any inference to it." Browning and the screenwriters might well have thought that incest had occurred, simply as part of their own understanding of the story, but it was *never* even implied in any extant script. Here is an important revelation.

In *Mark of the Vampire*, Tod Browning created one of the, if not *the*, most atmospheric horror movies of the 1930s, its ancient horrors of the distant past still able to resonate after all these decades. Some audience members might be disappointed in the revelation that the vampires are not real, but it is important to note that many others love the movie. After all, as the inspector tells Irena in the December 20 draft, "According to Shakespeare, we're all actors."

From Freaks to Timbuctoo

by Will Dodson

Tod Browning was still under contract to Metro-Goldwyn-Mayer after the box office disaster of *Freaks* (1932). He worked during much of 1932 on the story and script of *The Revolt of the Dead*, in collaboration with studio scripter Gerrit Lloyd and pulp writer Gouverneur Morris. *Revolt* was, of course, never produced. Instead, in a departure from his typical tales of the macabre, Browning was assigned in 1933 to direct *Fast Workers*, a sort of dramedy about skyscraper riveters who get mixed up with loose women. Based on the play *Rivets*, the film featured one of the final performances of John Gilbert.[3] Both the play and the screenplay raised the ire of the Production Code Administration (PCA) for morally ambiguous sexual situations. But MGM managed to keep an explicit lesbian joke and several direct sexual references in the finished film. For naught, it seems, as prurient interest did little to draw audiences. *Fast Workers* lost even more money — twice as much — as *Freaks*. *Freaks* lost $164,000, *Fast Workers* lost $360,000.

Subsequently, Browning began pre-production of a bayou-based thriller called *Louisiana Lou*, to be adapted by William Faulkner from Lea David Freeman's play *Ruby*. But Faulkner was fired, and then Browning. The reasons for their dismissal are unrecorded. (*Louisiana Lou* evolved into *Lazy River* [1934], directed by George B. Seitz.) Browning

Two views of Lavond (Lionel Barrymore) in disguise as Madame Mandilip.

then made a small-scale comeback, returning to his thematic strengths in 1935 with *Mark of the Vampire,* starring his longtime collaborator Lionel Barrymore and a mostly mute Bela Lugosi. Something of a mash-up of *London After Midnight* (1927) and *Dracula* (1931), *Mark* made a modest profit.

Eddie Mannix, Browning's producer, gave him the opportunity to choose his next project. Browning went to work on a treatment titled *The Witch of Timbuctoo,* loosely based on Abraham Merritt's *Burn Witch Burn!* (1932). His co-writer was Guy Endore, author of the novel *The Werewolf of Paris* (1933) and recently a regular contributor to horror scripts: *Mark of the Vampire, The Raven* and *Mad Love,* all 1935.

The Browning-Endore treatment was radically rewritten over several screenplay drafts with extensive input from Production Code director Joseph Breen. Though the Code had been in effect since 1930, it didn't begin aggressively enforcing its own rules until after Breen assumed power in 1934. *Fast Workers* and *Mark of the Vampire,* therefore, fell on either side of the year that the Code grew teeth. By the time *The Witch of Timbuctoo* began production, studios had started changing scripts substantially to receive approval both prior to and after production. Browning's film was retitled *The Devil-Doll* and released in 1936, again to a small profit. It was Browning's penultimate film, followed in 1939 by *Miracles for Sale,* a semi-comedic murder mystery starring Robert Young.[4]

The Devil-Doll's original treatment seems to have been only tangentially inspired by Merritt's novel, though that is not in itself unusual. However, the drastic changes to the treatment through several drafts — due not only to Breen's directives but also concerns from the British Board of Film Censors — reveal the extent to which the PCA and foreign market censors could alter films both prior to and during production.

Burn Witch Burn!

Abraham Merritt (1884-1943) was one of the most popular fantasy writers of his day. H.P. Lovecraft cited Merritt as a literary influence, and Gary Gygax called him one of his inspirations in creating the fantasy role-playing game *Dungeons & Dragons.* Merritt cut an eccentric figure, according to his biographer Sam Moskowitz, an editor of science fiction anthologies. Obsessed with the supernatural, Merritt amassed a library of over 5000 volumes on occult subjects, and cultivated an extensive garden of rare and poisonous plants used in history and lore for magical spells and mystical rites. A well-regarded journalist and editor of *The American Weekly,* Merritt kept exotic musical instruments in the office, and occasionally broke them out for staff members to play. He also reportedly kept a selection of equally exotic cheeses in the office, though this stash seems to have been for his personal use.[5]

Merritt claimed to have confirmed many of the supernatural phenomena described in his novels and short stories. In an unpublished essay about his research for *Burn Witch Burn!,* he described visiting a group of Pennsylvania Dutch who performed a "de-hexing" ritual on a young girl.[6] That experience, he suggested, influenced his conception of the novel's essential theme: a scientific mind coming to grips both with the existence of the supernatural, and the relative limits of known science in the face of the unexplainable. Merritt also drew on Fitz-James O'Brien's short story "The Wondersmith" (1859), about a toymaker using black magic to create living dolls, and sending them out to murder children.

Burn Witch Burn! appeared in serial form in *Argosy* magazine in 1932; Merritt turned it into a novel, and several editions were published between 1933 and 1935. The story is told as a first-person account by Dr. Lowell, a famous neurologist, who is enlisted by gangster Julian Ricori to investigate the bizarre murder of an associate. The victim first fell into a state of paralysis, followed by frightening facial contortions, death and an unnaturally rapid rigor mortis. Ricori calls it witchcraft, but Lowell rejects that explanation out of hand as superstitious nonsense. There have been several such deaths lately. The victims are seemingly unrelated, except that each had purchased a doll from a shop owned by an enormous, mustachioed hag named Madame Mandilip.

The character of Malita underwent several changes from script to screen. Originally, she was conceived as the mad doctor planning to become the "Queen of the World," but by the time the film began shooting, she had been reduced to scientist Marcel's half-mad wife. In this scene, Malita (played by Rafaela Ottiano) injects her tiny dog, which appears to be a Great Pyrenees.

⌒⌒●⌒⌒

Mandilip, aided by her pale, nervous niece Laschna, lures customers to the shop's back room where, through an elaborate spell, she curses them with a malady that paralyzes and kills them. Upon death, their souls and likenesses transfer into her dolls. The living dolls subsequently carry out Mandilip's murderous bidding. Lowell pursues Mandilip with the help of Ricori and his underworld associates. Lowell is arrogant and imperious, refusing to believe in magic or even take precautions as he confronts Mandilip, and he nearly succumbs

to her witchery. At the last moment, a doll resists Mandilip's control and attacks her. This distracts her long enough for Ricori to push her into a fireplace and snarl, "Burn, witch, burn!"[7] The story ends with Ricori asking Lowell if his scientific explanations can account for all he's seen, and Lowell, humbled, says they cannot.

The Witch of Timbuctoo

To say the film was loosely based on *Burn Witch Burn!* would be something of an understatement. The initial *Witch of Timbuctoo* treatment retained only the concept of turning people into living dolls, which now are under the control of an African witch.[8] Browning and Endore removed the conflict between science and the supernatural, and instead concocted a story of a man, wrongly imprisoned, exacting revenge while disguised in drag as a dollmaker.

Their treatment went through at least three drafts between January and May of 1935. Examining the revisions offers a fascinating glimpse at Browning and Endore's writing process. The first draft, a 38-page treatment dated January 17 through 31, is strange and horrific, perhaps even more so in contrast to the completed picture. A Frenchman, Jean Madres, escapes from Devil's Island with a companion named Ba-oola, described as "a Negro of fine physique." The two dig up corpses of white and black inmates from the prison graveyard and exchange clothes with them to fool the pursuing posse, led by a sadistic captain. Ba-oola is sick and exhausted as the two make their way to his home. Ba-oola's mother Nyleta is a powerful witch, and Nyleta's father is the most powerful witch doctor in Africa. Ba-oola begs Madres to take a package containing some hair and a shirt from the prison captain and give it to Nyleta so that the captain's cruelty "will be rewarded — suitably."

The scene shifts to Paris where, with Madres now officially "dead," his "widow" Marie and daughter Charlotte, accompanied by Charlotte's beau Raoul, go to an administrative building to receive her husband's belongings, We learn here that Madres had been a bank executive, and that his fellow board directors Radeu and Collet framed him for theft, resulting in his imprisonment. Marie and Charlotte lament that he was never able to prove his innocence, and that Raoul's family will never allow him to marry Charlotte due to the disgrace of the Madres name.

Madres and the recovered Ba-oola attend a ceremony in which Nyleta and the ancient witch doctor fashion a hand-shaped candle out of animal and human fat, with wicks made of the captain's hair. Nyleta tries the spell and fails; her father must complete the incantation. (Nyleta's relative weakness in this early draft makes her dependent upon and dominated by the male characters.) We then cut to a shot of the Devil's Island captain, in a coma, slowly shrinking. The spell curses him to shrink to four feet tall, for which he will be "the laughing stock of everyone" for the rest of his life.

To prove to Madres the effectiveness of the magic, Nyleta and the witch doctor show him a doll-sized tribesman; he was a rival chief until

he angered the witch doctor. Fascinated, Madres wants to use this power to revenge himself on Radeu and Collet. Ba-oola and the witch doctor compel Nyleta to accompany Madres to Paris, to repay him for saving Ba-oola from prison. Nyleta is at first reluctant, since her powers are weak, but the witch doctor assures her that his spirit will aid her.

In Paris, Madres disguises himself as an old woman named Madame Genève. In this guise, he observes his daughter working dreary jobs as a shopgirl and barmaid. Though not guilty of the crime for which he was imprisoned, Madres is an unsympathetic character. His initial plan for revenge is particularly dark: He wants Nyleta to control Radeu's daughter, have her kill her father, and then face the guillotine herself. (This complex plan resembles the one in Browning's *West of Zanzibar* [1928].) Nyleta points out that the magic cannot make someone do anything that's not in their character.

Madame Genève and Nyleta go to a bar to watch a gypsy dance performance: "There is one — an apache — his vicious nature plainly written on his face — and his girl — dark-eyed, fierce — a sordid, sulky beauty." The pair connive to enslave the dancers. Nyleta attempts the spell but fails, prompting Madres to lash out at her. She tries again, and the witch doctor's spirit helps work the magic. They shrink the dancers, as well as several others from the bar, to the size of dolls. Then, to test them, they have the dolls sneak into a bird shop and kill some parrots, finches and lovebirds in their cages.

After the shocking bird shop scene, Nyleta and Madres send out a doll who murders Radeu. In this version of the story, Marie and Charlotte know that Madres was not guilty of theft; but once he begins getting revenge, Marie weeps, as she says to Charlotte, "for your father's innocence." With Radeu gone, it will be harder to prove that Madres was falsely accused and wrongly imprisoned. Collet, fearing for his life, confesses to the police, but Madres is too far gone to care: He wants to kill Collet and complete his revenge. His savagery frightens Nyleta. When the doll botches the assassination of the imprisoned Collet, Madres loses his temper and throws Nyleta to the ground and

Left to right, Lionel Barrymore, Henry B. Walthall and Rafaela Ottiano. Love Ottiano's Bride of Frankenstein–style streak of white hair. About a month after *The Devil-Doll* wrapped, Walthall contracted a fatal case of influenza.

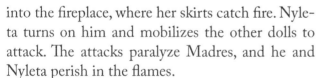

into the fireplace, where her skirts catch fire. Nyleta turns on him and mobilizes the other dolls to attack. The attacks paralyze Madres, and he and Nyleta perish in the flames.

The original story was much darker and more violent than the finished film, or even the source novel. The casual racism in the descriptions of the African tribe and Romani makes for a queasy read, even for its time. This is not to suggest that Browning and Endore were particularly racist in comparison to other filmmakers or white people, but to note that their racism pervades these treatments in troubling ways.[9] A second draft of the treatment, dated February 1, contained one significant change that added another morally dubious element. Here, Madame Genève and Nyleta go to see the dance in "a Bar Musette — notorious haunt of disreputable characters," thus explicitly locating the action in a house of sin.

Browning and Endore made significant changes in a 60-page third treatment, dated May 14 through June 11. Jean Madres is now Paul Duval; his blind mother Madame Duval believes in his innocence, but his wife and his daughter Charlotte think he's guilty. Raoul is willing to renounce his inheritance to marry Charlotte, but she will not allow it, and plans to run away where he cannot find her and share her misery. This time, three confederates frame Duval: Martin, Collet and Radeau (now spelled with an added "a"). The story retains direct mentions of suicide; for example, Charlotte tells Madame Duval that she wishes for the strength to kill herself.

The *Devil-Doll* conceit of Duval (Barrymore) disguising himself as an old woman was lifted from Browning's 1925 film *The Unholy Three* — as was this scene of a detective (Rollo Lloyd) nearly finding the stolen emerald hidden inside a clown doll.

Duval reveals himself to Madame Duval and vows revenge. Madame Duval begs him to let go of his hate. Duval's character is slightly more sympathetic this time around, though he remains hardened: "[H]e only intends to be just. …They must be made to suffer the seventeen years of imprisonment even as he did, and they must give him back all the money he might have been earning during those seventeen years." The Charlotte character takes a darker turn. Duval, disguised as an old woman peddling flowers, observes the Apache couple — the dancers of the first draft — dancing in a bar of ill repute, and notices Charlotte sitting in the bar, smoking a cigarette and drinking liquor. The male dancer sees her and yells at her for not "hustling out on the streets," making a clear implication that she is hooking. Duval realizes that his daughter's only chance to escape this life is to marry Raoul; and for that to happen, she must believe in her father's innocence. Thus, Duval has an added motive for clearing his name.

There is a short scene of Nyleta communing with the witch doctor, who hesitates because "he can see a bad end to all this." When Nyleta turns the Apache couple into dolls, the girl is described as "a tiny nude figure," a detail that Breen did not miss. In this version of the treatment, Radeau is renamed Collet, and Madame Genève peddles a doll to his little daughter, in order to infiltrate the family home. Once Collet is killed, the detective learns about the unusual dolls from Francois, their butler, who remembers that the old doll woman commented on Collet's jewelry.

There's a pantomime scene of the doll-sized Apaches dancing together while Nyleta plays a music box. The male Apache handles the woman roughly, and she draws her tiny stiletto on him, much to Nyleta's amusement. The pantomime scene remains in slightly altered form in subsequent drafts. A policeman visits the shop and questions Duval. Afterwards, Duval argues with Nyleta about the plan and twists her arm, showing that he's becoming unraveled. On Christmas Eve, Martin, under police guard, loses his nerve and confesses, just as a doll hidden in a Christmas tree was preparing to strike. Duval's vindication is announced in the newspapers and he visits his rejoiceful mother. He tells her not to let Charlotte know that he's alive and in Paris. His vengeance has taken him over.

When Raoul's parents arrive, Duval hides. He overhears them apologize to Madame Duval and approve the marriage. Duval is moved to tears but he is still bent on killing Martin and Radeau, who are now in prison. Duval sends a doll to the prison to complete the plan, and the sequence is cross-cut with Charlotte and Raoul's wedding.[10] The doll paralyzes Martin, then moves towards Radeau's cell. When a guard notices it, the doll attacks him and he hurls it against the bars and breaks its back.

Duval returns in triumph to the shop and happily thanks Nyleta, offering her half of the jewels. Trembling with fear, she tells him that the doll has been killed, providing evidence linking Madame Genève to the crimes. Duval, enraged, strikes her down. He says they must destroy the shop so that he isn't connected to Genève. Just then, police cars arrive. Perhaps feeling guilty for having abused her, he gives Nyleta money and pushes her out the door. He sets the store on fire, killing himself in the process. The story ends with Charlotte and Raoul leaving on a train for their honeymoon.

From these treatments came the first screenplay draft, written by Garrett Fort and dated August 5 through August 28, 1935. (Fort had previously worked on Browning's *Outside the Law* [1930] and *Dracula* [1931] as well as James Whale's *Frankenstein* [1931].) The screenplay extends Duval and Ba-oola's escape from Devil's Island, and has the cruel captain — who uses a racial slur to refer to Ba-oola — wire the prefect in Paris, Duval's likely destination. There's a scene in which Collet, Radeau and Martin discuss the newspaper reports of Duval's escape. Charlotte's beau is now Chico, a taxi driver with big dreams of owning his own taxi company. The character offers up some comic relief and innuendo with Charlotte — for example, he comments on his car's "loose rear-end." It's also revealed that Charlotte's mother killed herself in shame, so Charlotte lives with her blind grandmother. Charlotte hates her father, blaming him not just for the crime but for her mother's death.

Nyleta is stronger in Fort's screenplay. Here Ba-oola and the old witch doctor defer to her as their matriarch, and she is the sole magic user. The voodoo ceremony dispenses with the animal and human fats, substituting tamer fare (rice and wine). Much of the basic plot remains true to the previous treatment. Fort includes a few sentimental details, most notably that Duval used to love listening to Christmas carols with young Charlotte. When Duval learns that she now hates this memory, his craving for vengeance grows. In this version, after sending the dolls to kill Radeau and his wife, Duval breaks up the stolen jewelry while Nyleta watches the dolls dance. The woman doll falls off the table by accident.

In a tense-comedic scene, the policeman comes to the shop to question Madame Genève and begins shaking the *papier-mâché* doll in which the jewels are hidden. Instead of implying that Charlotte is a prostitute, this script makes her a waitress at a dive bar. However, there is a scene in which an older woman bartender (Charlotte's madam?) gives her grief for not being "friendly enough" to the customers.

Martin's confession doesn't satisfy Duval, who assumes that Martin's famous attorney will save him from prison. He seethes in anger, shouting to his mother that he will make them all suffer as they made him suffer. Charlotte, kicked out of the bar, arrives home drunk and interrupts his tirade. As Duval puts Charlotte to bed, she says she's ashamed of herself for not believing in her father's innocence, which is why she got drunk. Chastened, Duval decides not to go through with his plan to kill Martin. But overzealous Nyleta has already sent the doll on its mission. As in the treatment, the doll is killed and provides evidence of Genève's involvement.

Duval tells Nyleta to flee while he tries to burn the evidence. He sets the shop on fire, presumably killing himself. A gendarme sees Nyleta and tries to apprehend her. Nyleta's escape, then, casts suspicion on her rather than Genève. In the final scene, Charlotte and Chico talk sadly about the lost Madame Genève. The scene cuts to a long shot of Duval – or is it Duval's spirit? – looking out of a window as the sun shines down upon him. He's listening to the Christmas carols, hand out to his side as though clasping another's.

Censor the Witch! The Witch Is Dead!

Fort added several details to lend a melancholy sentimentality to Duval and Charlotte's relationship. He also cut some of the treatment's most disturbing images, including the bird shop attack. Nevertheless, the screenplay ran into major trouble with Breen. In a September 13 letter, he lists in minute detail elements that must be eliminated for the script to be approved. Most of his complaints are about bits of business, such as a side character referred to as a "pansy," but he grows more strident as the list goes on. Most notably, he objected to the intimation of Duval's suicide, writing that it would be "most advisable" for Duval to be captured and subject to legal trial. Alternatively, Breen suggests that Duval can attempt to fight off the police, and they can kill him. Either way was fine with him.

Breen also objected to Charlotte's circumstances, arguing that dialogue and situations should make clear that "her own character is perfectly pure, although the work she must do is sordid and distasteful." Further, costumes should be tailored modestly, there should be no nudity (not even doll nudity), and at no time should a woman gowned in her underwear provide "offensive exposure." This note is in reference to a scene of Charlotte working in a laundry while in the background, a laundress lifts wet bloomers out of the wash. Breen also took issue with the scene of Duval breaking up the sto-

len jewelry, because it offered instruction in how to commit a crime. Finally, and somewhat jarringly, Breen wrote, "The suggestion of Nyleta's ample breasts resting on the edge of the table is objectionable." I read every extant treatment and script available in the Margaret Herrick Library and was unable to find a suggestion of Nyleta's ample breasts in any of them. It is possible that Breen's sensuous imagination exceeds my own.

MGM turned the script over to staff writers, who worked independently and re-shaped the story. First, an uncredited Robert Chapin wrote a revised screenplay (dated October 30 through November 15) that addressed some of Breen's objections. Chapin, for reasons unknown, makes a few name changes: Genève is now Madame Mandilip, and Chico is now called Toto. Chapin softens the explicit racism, removing the captain's slur, and then enhances the implicit racism, for example, having Ba-oola proudly point out that while other tribes are cannibals, his own is not. Duval also clearly indicates his repulsion for the animalistic ceremony. He may be bloodthirsty for revenge, but he's still "civilized." Duval asks Nyleta to accompany him to Paris as a favor, and she agrees on the condition that she be given one of the dolls of his enemies, because "[a] long time have I wanted the great power of a white 'doll.'" Duval eagerly offers her all three of the conspirators.

Now disguised as Madame Mandilip, Duval meets his daughter as she enters the doll shop to sell flowers. Charlotte still dances at a cafe and wears what is described as "a very revealing costume." In addition, she flirts with three boorish men at the café who turn out to be Radeau, Collet and Martin. Their dialogue reveals that they cheat on their wives with women at the cafe, underscoring their low characters. The relationship between Nyleta and Duval is more tense, as he continues to be put off by her ceremonies and she grows impatient to get her white doll. Nyleta grows more menacing the longer she waits.

The most substantive change is, in fact, Duval's fate. Toto, who had grown suspicious of Madame Mandilip, snoops around in the doll shop, and Nyleta captures him. Duval comes on the scene as Nyleta prepares to turn Toto into a doll. Duval confronts

Lavond (Barrymore), disguised as Mandilip, reconnects with his daughter Lorraine (Maureen O'Sullivan).

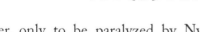

her, only to be paralyzed by Nyleta's magic. A dazed Toto escapes to find Charlotte and the detective. The three return to the now-deserted shop and the scene ends with a fade-out of Toto's arm closed around Charlotte. Duval pays for his crimes when he becomes the white doll Nyleta had so desired. Chapin's revision of the Garrett Fort script is sharp, and retains most of the macabre details and understated humor of the Browning-Endore treatments.

Alas, the script was bound for a complete overhaul. In a November 11 telegram, overseas sales agent Dave Blum tells the head of MGM's story department, Samuel Marx, about the "quiet talk" he had with the British censor. The censor noted that while "converting human beings to [the] size of dolls is legitimate drama," no black magic could be shown at all. Blum identified a quick fix from a suggestion Marx had made earlier: "DUVAL MEETS SCIENTIST OR DOCTOR AT DEVIL'S ISLAND INSTEAD BLACK MAN." The telegram emphasizes the inherent racism toward black representation in film in general, in this case, African characters caricatured as tribes of savage voodoo witch doctors. In this case, the racial caricature was removed in order to avoid prohibited images of black magic. Another scriptwriter would have to be brought on to completely revise the story.

The Devil-Doll

That scriptwriter was Erich von Stroheim, the once extravagant auteur, now reduced to studio script doctor. It seems likely that von Stroheim was working on the screenplay at the same time as Chapin, since his revision is dated November 19, 1935, just a few days after Chapin's. However, von Stroheim must have gotten the message from Blum and Marx, because his version jettisons Nyleta and the African magic, develops more of the Duval family's past, and softens some of the objectionable material. Since Nyleta is no more, the film could not be called *The Witch of Timbuctoo*, and so it was changed to *The Devil-Doll*.

Von Stroheim biographer Richard Koszarski minimized his contribution to the script, citing the 1974 book *Classics of the Horror Film* in which William K. Everson wrote that the most likely von Stroheim contribution to *The Devil-Doll* was "a wisecrack about the Christmas season always bringing out religious fanatics."[11] In fact, Everson suggested that von Stroheim's contribution was much more extensive. The differences between the Fort and Chapin scripts and von Stroheim's offer concrete proof, the least of which being von Stroheim's typical length: His script was 211 pages, compared to Fort's 125 and Chapin's 129! In addition to the crack about Christmas, Everson wrote that the backdrop of "having tragedy and evil played out against a Christmas tinsel motif" and an emphasis on Duval paying the price for his sins seems particularly consistent with von Stroheim's style. Everson did not have the benefit of the script in making his conjecture, but he seems to have been correct. Film scholar Bret Wood's 1992 examination of the archived scripts notes elements of von Stroheim's characteristic "brutal realism."[12]

Von Stroheim came up with a new opening scene for the film, set in the Duval family's Paris home. Paul and his daughter Lorraine (no longer Charlotte) prepare to celebrate mother Helene's birthday; Paul has bought her a beautiful necklace. As the mail arrives, he is pleased to see an invitation to dine with the bank president. Life is good. Paul then goes to work at the bank, where his clerks greet him strangely, half-heartedly. He enters his office and finds the police waiting for him. Collet, Radeau and Martin accuse him of an unnamed crime. We cut to a courtroom, where he is sentenced to hard labor on Devil's Island. The Duvals' home is auctioned, including Helene's birthday necklace. To twist the knife even further,

Collet is shown bidding on the necklace.

Duval escapes from the prison, joined by a sick man named Marco. There's a new scene between the prison director and the captain in which they try to cover up the escape, but the news somehow gets out, as the next scenes show Collet, Radeau and Martin discussing the newspaper article announcing that Duval is at large.

As in the previous drafts, Lorraine is reluctant to marry Toto because she is ashamed of her father. A new scene, which becomes a motif in this screenplay, has Toto take Lorraine to the top of the Eiffel Tower. Toto points out how small people are from their vantage point, and argues that no person is big enough to prevent her happiness.

The story cuts back to Duval's escape, as he and Marco make their way through a swamp, searching for the home of Marco's mother. In the distance, they hear organ music, and Marco rejoices because his mother, Dr. Malita, plays the organ to give her inspiration in her experiments. As Marco puts it, "Mother is a very <u>unusual</u> woman!" Marco is not kidding. Malita's swamp shack is guarded by a "hoard of ferocious looking 'chow-chow' dogs," and she's served by a "ghastly" albino woman named Lachna. Dr. Malita discusses her experiments with the two men: She's shrinking animals to the size of toys, in preparation for doing the same to humans. As a side effect of the process, the subjects lose their will and must be controlled by the doctor. She is looking for a way to eliminate that side effect. Her motive in this draft appears to be global conquest: "When I have reduced every human being in the world — and I shall be the only normal person left? I shall be 'Queen of the World'!" Duval begins musing to himself on the viability of these living dolls as assassins…

The script now takes us to Paris, and Madame Mandilip's shop, where Malita has accompanied Duval, back in drag, to exact his revenge. It's revealed that Lorraine works in a laundry, and that Helene died of grief rather than by suicide. After Duval reveals himself to his mother, he gets the wheels of vengeance in motion: Radeau and Collet are quickly dispatched by the dolls. Upon hearing of Martin's confession to the police, Duval thinks he'll be able to return to his previous station, in-

Blossoming romance between young Lorraine (Maureen O'Sullivan) and Toto (Frank Lawton).

cluding resuming his job at the bank—but he still plans on having Martin killed. Madame Duval mourns that while before Duval was innocent but wronged, now he is guilty of murder, and she convinces him to spare Martin. But Malita is already at the prison, making the failed assassination attempt detailed in earlier drafts.

The finale has Duval and Malita in the basement workshop, where Duval douses everything with kerosene and sets the shop on fire to destroy any evidence that could link him to the crimes. Malita tries to escape, but Duval drags her into the back room with him so that they will die together. A doll stabs Malita, and Duval dies clutching his rosary. In a nod to the earlier scene of Toto and Lorraine on the Eiffel Tower, the script ends with the couple heading to the top of the Eiffel Tower to watch the sunrise.

Now MGM had placated the British censors, but also had an unwieldy script that needed paring down. Yet another writer, Richard Schayer, was brought in, and he submitted a draft dated February 7 through 25, 1936. He chopped the script down to 142 pages, removing Stroheim's lengthy preamble and making several other changes, most notably to the Marco and Malita characters. Marco is now known as Marcel, a scientist aided by his wife Malita. Marcel has a mad but altruistic motive for wanting to shrink the world's population: He is concerned that humanity is fast depleting the world's resources, and by reducing them to doll size, he intends both to preserve the environment and ensure that everyone has food and shelter.[13] Marcel explains,

Duval, my friend — millions of years ago the creatures that roamed the world were gigantic in size, and as they multiplied, the earth could no longer produce enough food for them. The largest died off. Then evolution began reducing the size of all living things, until, with the dawn of civilization, mankind and his so-called science began blocking the progress of evolution. But still all living creatures multiplied, until today we are back at the beginning — millions are starving, million more are homeless…

But, my friend Duval, if we can succeed with what we are trying to do, we can with one stroke bridge the gap in evolution's advance — think of it, Duval — all living creatures reduced to one-sixth their size — the human race — only so tall— …Then there would be food for all — homes for all — think of it, Duval — think of it!

Marcel shows Duval a collection of doll-sized dogs, and then miniaturizes Lachna. After Marcel has a fatal heart attack. Malita agrees to help Duval on the condition that he help her realize Marcel's vision. They bring Lachna along, in order to use her as his miniaturized assassin. The rest of the screenplay hews to von Stroheim's outline, but trimming much of his grandiloquent dialogue. The climax has Duval poisoning Malita, burning the shop to the ground, and dissolving Malita's body, as well as his own, in acid! Mandilip's "journal" has been behind for the police to discover, thereby pinning the crimes on her and putting Duval in the clear. The script ends with a married Toto and Lorraine in front of a fireplace, their little son Toto Jr. warming his bare behind at the fire.

Breen Gets to the Bottom of It

By this time, Browning's original story was all but unrecognizable, and the screenplay had a schizophrenic tone, leaping from science fiction to the macabre to the camp to the sentimental. But even after these extensive revisions, Joseph Breen still had objections and detailed them in a February 12, 1936, letter. Given the date, it's unclear if Breen was responding to the von Stroheim script or a version of Schayer's. Breen repeated his objection from earlier drafts that the doll could not be shown stabbing Collet; also, "[t]here should be no horrifying sound used" to imply Collet's fear or his death. Breen also reiterated that it should not be implied that Lorraine was a "loose woman," and that Duval should not be shown breaking up the stolen jewelry. Finally, Breen tut-tutted, "The business of showing the infant Toto's bare behind must be deleted."[14]

Principal photography took place in March and April 1936. Then more revisions were made and scenes re-shot. Leon Gordon, one of *Freaks'* screenwriters, is credited with work dated May 15 through May 18. "Duval" became "Lavond," Radeau became Radin, and Collet, Coulvet. In a short new Devil's Island scene, Lavond tells Marcel that *hate* has kept him alive all these years — hate for the men who framed him. In another new scene, Malita teaches Lavond to control the dolls with his mind. Lavond reveals his identity to Toto and convinces him to keep his secret. The most significant change was a new ending. Malita tries to kill Lavond and accidentally burns the shop to the ground, presumably dying in it. Lavond survives and mails a confession signed "Mandilip" to the police. Then, with Toto's help, he meets with Lorraine and says his goodbyes, though he does not reveal his identity to her. Finally, Lavond walks alone to a bridge over the Seine:

> Moving slower now — more shambling. The background we see is a bridge. FULL CAMERA BACK until we come to a fairly CLOSE SHOT OF HIS FACE. No tragedy here — almost an ethereal light as he looks toward the water. He is looking over the parapet of the bridge with the dark swiftly running waters of the Seine below. We see him slowly mount to the top of the parapet. MUSIC RISES TO A DRAMATIC TEMPO. He stands swaying for a moment.
>
> QUICK DISSOLVE TO:
>
> JUST A FEW FEET OF THE SWIFTLY RUNNING DARK WATERS OF THE

SEINE BELOW THE BRIDGE —

But no sign of Lavond is visible. Light this, giving us the effect that a cloud is just passing over the moon and its rays slowly and beautifully illuminated the water. MUSIC REACHES A CRESCENDO AS WE — FADE OUT.

The obvious suicide made MGM nervous about the British censors and the Breen Office.[15] A second set of retakes, credited to William Anthony McGuire and Sam Zimbalist, added a new scene with Lavond making it clear to Malita that he has no intention of helping her shrink the world's population, and that he intends to destroy their workshop and go into exile. As he explains, "In proving my innocence, I've forever condemned myself. We must go away. And before we leave, we must destroy all this." Malita, now completely mad, attacks him and burns down the shop as in the previous draft. The film concludes with Toto asking Lavond what he will do next:

LAVOND

Where I'm going I won't need money. ... Look — the sun is almost down.

TOTO

It will be up again tomorrow.

LAVOND

Will it?

(then softly)

I wonder.

(then trying to be gay)

Goodbye, Toto.

Now the implication of Lavond's suicide is much more ambiguous. Does he kill himself or wander in exile? Given the PCA's well-known aversion to suicide, it is interesting to note how many of the scripts included a character's suicide, either of the protagonist's wife or himself, across several drafts and several writers. Even the retakes, while ambiguous, imply that Lavond will end his own life.

Finally, it seems, the implication was ambiguous enough, and the script completely free of baby bot-

Browning and the cross-dressed Lionel Barrymore on the *Devil-Doll* set.

toms: In a June 25, 1936, letter, Breen enclosed the Production Code Certificate of Approval No. 2328 for *The Devil-Doll*. He couldn't resist adding one last note: "However, we suggest that you delete the scene showing the breaking up of the stolen jewelry...." Some scenes MGM was willing to stand up for, apparently.

The *Devil-Doll* reviews were more or less positive, and highlighted the unusual nature of the story; the advanced special effects work, the doll scenes' oversized sets and Lionel Barrymore's performance. Abraham Merritt was dismissive of *The Devil-Doll*, and of movies in general. Years later, in a letter to one of his editors, he commented, "I did not like [*The Devil-Doll*]. They were forced by English censorship to change the scenario from one of straight witchcraft into a pseudo-scientific one. ... In my opinion few motion pictures are worth the trouble of seeing." Merritt also mentioned that he

Malita (Ottiano) listens as Lavond (Barrymore), out of his Mandilip makeup, reads aloud from a Paris newspaper about the plight of their latest victim.

joined *Dracula* and the unproduced *The Revolt of the Dead* as the only Browning films with actual supernatural elements. In most others — including *The Thirteenth Chair* (1929), Browning's first sound picture and first to feature Lugosi — magic is a scam, a ruse by carnies and crooks to separate rubes from their money.

The Witch of Timbuctoo also would have presented a major casting challenge. It's possible that black actors would have been cast as the tribal characters and depicted in a manner similar to the natives in Browning's *West of Zanzibar* (1928), which featured black actors as members of a cannibal tribe, some individuals with significant supporting roles and screen time. Ba-oola is a larger role, and Nyleta has as much dialogue and screen time as Madres/Duval. Would a white actor and actress have performed in black-face, or would a black actor and actress have been cast? Either way, the description of Nyleta in the treatments and screenplay suggest that it would have been a horribly racist portrayal.

As it is, little remains of *Timbuctoo*, and so one might reasonably ask, is *The Devil-Doll* really a Tod Browning picture? Bret Wood claimed that Browning lost interest in the picture: "Not only did he watch helplessly as the story was crassly cut apart and rewritten, he then had to film this bastardized script." No doubt Browning was disappointed and frustrated, though we do not have any of his comments recorded or reported by his collaborators.

But actress and long-time Browning friend Winifred Westover suggested that Browning was anything but apathetic during production. She said that when the oversized sets "weren't built exactly

considered the movie *Dr. Cyclops* (1940) a steal from both *Burn Witch Burn!* and *The Devil-Doll*.

Had the Browning-Endore-Fort screenplay been produced, *The Witch of Timbuctoo* would have been fascinating for Browning enthusiasts. In many respects, it represents a culminating Browning picture: a mix of the macabre and melodramatic, an exotic locale, a fraught father-daughter relationship, a baroque revenge plot, and the redemption of its perpetrator. In other respects, however, it would have been quite unusual. It would have

to Browning's meticulous calculations, and when rushes showed that the scenes in question looked preposterous, he had the sets struck and completely rebuilt."[16] Perhaps Browning was simply trying to make a commercially successful picture, to keep his professional momentum going. Yet, despite the drastic changes from story to screen, *The Devil-Doll* retains many themes and motifs, and cribbed scenes, which run throughout Browning's work.

Browning manages to present the strange and bizarre as normal, and highlight the malice of the "normal" as represented by the sinister capitalists Radin,[17] Coulvet and Martin. The manic Malita and vengeful Lavond's plot is handled as if it were a totally reasonable reaction to Lavond's situation. Browning even manages to make the "scientific" process of shrinking humans look like a magic trick, making a production of shrouding the dolls in cotton gauze and mist as the shrinking process begins. It was hampered by censors, altered by script doctors, and subjected to reshoots, but *The Devil-Doll* is still quintessential Browning.

"Civilization Is Doomed!": Tod Browning and The Revolt of the Dead

by Gary D. Rhodes

Tod Browning in the early 1930s.

Of all of Tod Browning's film narratives, the never-made *The Revolt of the Dead* definitely ranks among the most bizarre. In different versions of its evolving script drafts, a woman suffers possession and stigmata before being crucified, and the dead nearly displace the living on planet Earth. A surviving treatment, script, page revisions and notations from Browning's personal archive offer key insights into the strange and eerie horror film that might have been.

Press coverage of *The Revolt of the Dead* was minimal. On November 1, 1932, *The Hollywood Reporter* told readers that MGM would produce the film with Browning as director. According to the news item, he was also co-author of the script with Gerrit Lloyd. For D.W. Griffith, Lloyd had written or co-written *The Drums of Love* (1928), *Lady of the Pavements* (1929) and *Abraham Lincoln* (1930). The *Hollywood Reporter* item also reported that the cast would "include many big names."

A syndicated Hollywood column published in the New Orleans *Times-Picayune* on November 7, 1932, briefly noted, "Tod Browning will direct *Revolt of Death* [*sic*], a story of reincarnation." The following day, *Variety* reported that Browning would direct a script being written by Gerrit Lloyd and Gouverneur Morris, the author of numerous pulp novels. Morris' 1913 novel *The Penalty* became a 1920 film starring Lon Chaney. And his story "The Purple Mask" was adapted into the Chaney film *The Ace of Hearts* (1921). Both movies were directed by Wallace Worsley.

A surviving copy of the *Revolt of the Dead* script, dated October 26, 1932, lists the authors as Lloyd and Morris, who had based their work on Browning's original story. Morris had been involved on the project for a few weeks prior to the mention of him in *Variety*, if not longer.

Browning's original story and the resultant script drew upon various sources, but a "non-fiction" newspaper article that Browning kept in his possession probably reveals its inspiration. Using information from Alexandra David-Néel's book *Magic and Mystery in Tibet* (1932), the article details that Asian country's mystical rituals. An ink notation (presumably made by Browning) draws attention to a sentence about the "peculiarly unpleasant ceremony in which corpses are brought to life" via Tibetan magic and "mystic dances." The article also describes how Tibetans use hypnotism and telepathy. These ideas are found in *The Revolt of the Dead*, the first part of which is set in Africa. (It is not known if Browning read David-Néel's book; her book and *The Revolt of the Dead* have a few similarities.)

The origin of Loogo's name is unknown. Presuming that the first syllable rhymed with "goo," the name might have stemmed from the first two syllables of Bela Lugosi's last name. Or perhaps it was a variation on the term "Lung-gom," which appears in the forementioned newspaper article based on David-Néel's book. Lung-gom was the alleged "name of the training which enables its adepts to take long journeys with surprising rapidity and to dance for days and nights without rest."

In what seems to be Browning's earliest treat-

With his adaptation of *Dracula* a recent moneymaker, Browning went back to that well during the writing of *The Revolt of the Dead*, creating characters instantly reminiscent of the vampire movie's Mina, Harker and (especially) Prof. Van Helsing. (Photo courtesy Heritage Auctions)

ment for *The Revolt of the Dead*, two Englishmen, Trelanny and Suffolk, work at a British outpost in Africa. They host a young and generally moral Polish man named Boris Zwsbisko, who is "deeply interested" in voodoo. Boris befriends a "very wise, very wicked witch doctor" named Loogo, who is capable of "raising the dead if they have not been dead too long." (*Magic and Mystery in Tibet* discusses magicians who were skillful at "dealing with the demons" and the "spirits of the dead." It also describes an educated Tibetan who works for the local British government; his occult interests led him to search for "supernormal powers.")

When Loogo slits a white child's throat as a sacrifice to the gods, Boris tries to stop him. Trelanny and Suffolk arrive and mistakenly believe Boris to be the murderer. For a crime he didn't commit, Boris is tried, found guilty and sentenced to be put to death. Awaiting his execution, Boris hatches a plan. Browning's first treatment explains:

> The graveyards of the world are filled with [the] dead who have been wronged by the living. Boris will come back from the dead. He will bring back the other dead who have been wronged and they will crowd the living out of the world.

Trelanny and Suffolk are unimpressed with such threats. A firing squad riddles Boris with bullets.

Thanks to Loogo's powers, Boris returns from the grave and boards a ship for England. There he meets Trelanny's sister Sylvia. After hypnotizing her, Boris makes Sylvia do "incredibly wicked things." More and more people rise from their graves. As Browning wrote, "It gets so that families are afraid to go home after the theater lest they find the late Aunt Agatha sitting in the chimney corner."

After seeing Boris and his henchmen literally crucify a man who refused to surrender his gold, Sylvia comes out of her hypnotic spell. Fleeing from the ghastly scene, she faints in the middle of a street. Her body features the marks of stigmata — wounds resembling those Jesus Christ suffered during the crucifixion.

At that point in the treatment, Browning switched voice and revealed that he didn't yet know how to end the story. The audience must learn that Loogo is ultimately to blame for these terrible events, but will the story switch back to Africa, where the witch doctor lives, or should Loogo travel to London? Browning concludes by asking, "These questions must be answered before we can engineer and climax the hanging scene, and have it all click."

The next surviving document is the October 26, 1932, script co-authored by Lloyd and Morris. Browning clearly had major input and made extensive notes on the same. The result is written in the style of an extended treatment with dialogue.

At times, it is particularly visual, as the following quotations suggest:

> Boris was seated in a chair, as dead as an Egyptian statue.

> [A]s quick as a rattlesnake, Von Hecklemetz struck.

> It is a fog of varying densities. It varied from light mist to a watery opaqueness.

The script is also quite literary, including in ways that would not have directly translated on-screen, but that might have helped Browning establish his desired atmosphere. Consider, for example, sentences like "The room smelled of the grave."

There are also descriptions that speak to Browning's obsessions. A doctor who wears an Inverness cape is "almost a hunch-back." The female victim and her father seem to possess psychic powers. And one character in London describes a peculiar event, as strange as any in Browning's cinema: "[A] shark has followed a ship all the way across the ocean and this time it wasn't only one shark. It was hundreds of sharks, thousands of them." The sharks followed the vessel into London, specifically because a dead man, Boris, was aboard.

The script features numerous changes and expansions to Browning's original idea. For example, the Polish Boris Zwsbisko became the Hungarian Boris Odeschalchi and then Boris Odelosi. Though his parents are still living, he would no longer be a particularly young character. Rather, he is

> a tall man with strong forceful features and there was something strange and unforgettable about him. His eyes at once shone with a fine intelligence and had in them a hint of madness.

Boris' character might have evolved to allow for Bela Lugosi to play the role. Here was a process that Browning understood from past practice. Casting Lugosi in *The Thirteenth Chair* (1929) required a switch from the original Irish character "Inspector Donahue" to the Indian "Inspector Delzante."

Other changes to Browning's first treatment abound. Trelanny's name has become Trelawney. And it is not his sister Sylvia that Boris victimizes in London, but rather Suffolk's sister Maud. Here

812-65

Cinephiles examining the *Revolt of the Dead* script will read that the character of Boris is Hungarian — and no doubt wonder if Browning had Bela (pictured here in *Mark of the Vampire*) in mind for the role. They might also wonder how Bela would have liked playing a character named Boris.

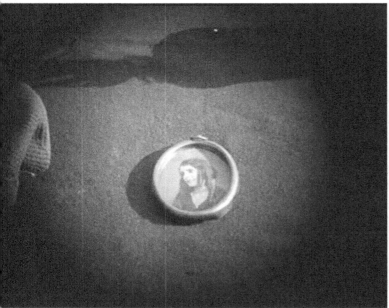

In *The Revolt of the Dead*, African witch doctor Loogo goes loco when he sees a photo of Suffolk's sister Mary and, after sailing to England on a steamer, seeks her out. Could the writers' inspiration have been *Nosferatu* (1922), in which the Transylvanian vampire Count Orlok sees a photo of Hutter's wife and becomes infatuated, just before setting sail for her native Germany?

is a logical change for dramatic purposes, given that in this version it is Suffolk who kills Boris, rather than a firing squad. Then the name Maud became Mary, presumably to heighten the religiosity implied in the evolving story.

The script also features clear descriptions for Loogo as well. He would not be a stereotypical witch doctor:

> Loogo wore none of the insignia of his calling. His face and body were not painted and his breech clout differed in no way from those worn by the other men of the tribe. His features … were thin and sharp. He had a commanding brow. His hair was snow white. He carried himself and moved with a certain majesty. Although his body was smooth and firm he looked to be a very old man.

Loogo speaks various languages, including Latin, even though he has physically never left Africa. His "astral body" has been a "great traveller."

Doris, a missionary's daughter "not more than three or four years old," is spirited away into the jungle by Boris and presented to Loogo, who keeps her in a hut "so cunningly and secretly hidden that it could not even have been seen from an airplane." Loogo's followers worship pagan gods at an altar made from human skulls. The congregation sways with demonic fervor. As the script notes, they "danced and contorted their bodies with the utmost conceivable demonstrations of violence, and they screamed at the tops of their lungs."

In preparation for sacrificing Doris, Loogo impales a dove on his knife. When a native woman takes the dove from him, voodoo drums begin to beat. The script details what happens next:

> In each hand she held one of the bird's wings and one of its legs. The rhythm of the drums increased in tempo and with it the movement of the girl's feet and body. As she danced she looked upward at the dove. The expression on her face was that of a Sadist, a torturer. Steadily the speed of the drum rhythm increased and with them the speed of the girl's dancing, and it looked to Boris as if she were trying to tear the dove apart.
>
> As the dove's breast tore apart and blood flowed, the girl's dancing went into a kind of frenzy. The blood ran down her arms and dropped on her upturned face. Suddenly the music of the drums came to a full stop

and so also the dancing of the girl. She bent forward, lower and lower until the dove was above the knife. Blood fell on the knife. Almost it seemed as if the dove were a sponge which the girl was wringing. When the knife had been sanctified with the blood of the dove, the drums again began to beat, this time with an incredible agitation and fury. The girl kept time with her feet and body, her face now like that of a maniac, upturned to the bleeding, mangled dove. The dance came to a sudden, and to Boris, an unexpected end. The girl gave one long piercing scream and fell to the floor in convulsions.

The drums stop beating. The intensity of the scene unfolds in a manner not dissimilar to the later voodoo ritual depicted in Alan Parker's *Angel Heart* (1987).

Boris is amazed by Loogo's occult powers, as well as by his followers, one of them a dead man who seems "sightless, without thought" and who wears "garlands of withered flowers hung about his neck and loins." Boris mistakes him for a zombie, but Loogo responds scornfully. "A Zombie … is only a wretched man who has been drugged. That is a dead man who has come back."

It is evident that Browning was interested in voodooism and pagan rituals, which he had explored in the silent *West of Zanzibar* (1928) with Lon Chaney, a film that director William J. Cowen

remade as a talkie, *Kongo*, in 1932. *Kongo* was released in October, while Browning was working in earnest on *The Revolt of the Dead*. Approximately two months earlier, United Artists had released Victor Halperin's *White Zombie* (1932), the first feature film about zombies. Browning apparently wanted his new project to surpass the thrills and horrors of such competition.

In his prior movies, including *Dracula* (1931), Browning had showed little or no blood on-screen. Not so with *The Revolt of the Dead*:

> Into a bowl which contained a dark liquid, blood perhaps, Loogo dipped the forefinger of his right hand and, occasionally refreshing his supply of pigment, enclosed the black skull which he had already painted on the breast of Boris with a broad dark circle.

The implication is that the liquid is the blood of Doris, the child who has just been murdered.

The dead returned to life have no soul, but Loogo is able to transport his own soul into them, at least temporarily. (In a section titled "The Corpse Who Dances," the book *Magic and Mystery in Tibet* describes a similar process, the "*trong jug*" rite, which allows the spirit "of another being to pass into a corpse and apparently resuscitate it, though the corpse is not animated by its original occupant.") The witch doctor deeply desires to bring other corpses back from the grave. "There *will* be more of them," he vows, "hundreds of them, thousands of them." Boris becomes a candidate for resurrection after Suffolk, who knows that Boris kidnapped the child, shoots and kills him in a fit of rage. Boris' body is brought to Loogo, and the witch doctor begins to work his magic:

> Upon the knitted brow and the commanding face of the witch doctor was an expression of concentration so powerful that it amounted to torment. He was urging the dead man to come back. He was urging the warm vital current which controls locomotion to pass from the body of the dancing girl into that of the dead man. But the dead man lay still and his wide open eyes were glazed and dead.

Continued on page 86

On this page and the next are illustrations from a newspaper article found alongside Browning's *Revolt of the Dead* script in the director's papers; this now-yellowed article was apparently one of his inspirations. The first illustration, below, shows the opening text. Beneath the other three illustrations, in quotes, are the newspaper's original captions.

A French Woman Explorer Describes How They Live Naked in Zero Temperatures by "Generating Their Own Heat," Run Incredible Distances Without Rest, Food or Drink, Talk to Each Other Many Miles Apart—But, If They Do, Science Doesn't Believe There Is Any "Magic" About It

"Tibetan Dancers Representing Skeletons and Whose 'Dances of Death' Form a Part of the Training of the Tibetan Mystics and Magicians."

"A Tibetan 'Mystic' Standing Naked Among the Snows of the Himalayas."

"A Lama Beginning a 'Magic' Rite, Dressed as a Goddess."

Continued from page 83

Though it takes time and effort, Boris sits upright, his corpse returned to life. But here is life without soul. Despite some difficulty, Loogo controls him. The two board a steamer ship bound for London, the master of the dead man pretending to be the servant of a living person.

Browning's cinema was often about trickery and pretenses, but he also valued historical accuracy, ranging from the depiction of the Aya Sophia mosque in *The Virgin of Stamboul* (1920) to the use of the Hungarian language on signage in *The Mystic* (1925). In his talkies, Browning had non–English characters speak in other languages, such as the Asian character in *Outside the Law* (1930). He used authentic footage of Madison Square Garden in *Iron Man* (1931) and he cast real sideshow performers in *Freaks* (1932). In the *Revolt of the Dead* script, the Sackville Club is mentioned; it was an actual gentlemen's club that opened in London in 1794.

More than anything else, though, the characters' journey is reminiscent of Browning's *Dracula*, with the supernatural monster coming from an allegedly uncivilized region (Transylvania) to a noted city in Western civilization (London). By that point, the script has already drawn upon *Dracula* in minor respects, from its invocation of the supernatural to a key aspect of Loogo's African altar. It features a "blue flame," the same burning color that prominently appears in Bram Stoker's *Dracula* (1897).

The similarities become more specific and pronounced during the London scenes. For example, Loogo stays in a decaying old home, its floors "thick with dust." It is reminiscent of Carfax Abbey:

> In a suburb of London in the midst of old dilapidated grounds and lawns which had not been trimmed, stood a gloomy three-story house in the Georgian manner. The house had not been occupied for many years. In the cellars under it, dating to a previous century, much of the house's furnish-

Had *The Revolt of the Dead* been made, Loogo would have taken his place on the list of Golden Age Horror fiends able to telepathically control the girl "long distance": Dracula, Svengali, *White Zombie*'s Murder and *The Mummy*'s Imhotep (pictured).

ings had been stored. There was a confusion of chairs, tables, packing cases, etc.

The home is situated near the Suffolk family residence, with Loogo desiring the nearby Mary just as Dracula desires Mina.

Mary is in love with Dr. Martin, much as Mina is in love with Jonathan Harker. (And, like Mina, Mary asks that she be killed if the situation becomes too horrible.) Into the mix comes insanity, with Suffolk's letter to Mary reading as if he is "mad," his minor character now representing something of a Renfield. Thanks to Loogo's powers, Mary falls ill, similar to Mina after meeting Dracula. Under hypnotic control, Mary tries to embrace Dr. Martin and look deep into his eyes, somewhat reminiscent of a *Dracula* scene between Mina and Harker.

There is also the clash of modern science with the occult, not unlike the divide that initially exists between *Dracula*'s Dr. Seward (Herbert Bunston) and Prof. Van Helsing (Edward

hypnotism into the realm of possession. As the professor explains, "Some demonic force may have attacked [Mary]." Consider the following passage, which describes actions that wouldn't appear on-screen in Hollywood until decades later, in films like William Friedkin's *The Exorcist* (1973):

> Her deep gasps and wrenching movements told the doctors of the extreme effort she was making to defend herself against the power that was attacking her. Then a great trembling shook her body, the desperate commotion of being overcome. Her forehead lowered into wrinkles. Her eyes took on a sharp and cunning and penetrating hardness. Her mouth writhed with an evil vigor.

Elsewhere, we learn that an "unholy spirit … possesses her," the language and descriptions being evocative of an actual demonic possession, to the extent that she speaks at one point with the voice of Loogo: "THE GRAVE WILL GIVE UP ITS OWN, UNTIL THE WORLD WILL BE FILLED WITH THE WALKING DEAD." According to the script, such a development would cause the living to go insane.

The religiosity intrinsic in such a possession becomes heightened when Mary undergoes stigmata. The fact that her body and soul have been infected requires the professor to resort to a particularly surprising plan. He will use a mallet and spikes to crucify Mary, an act that will cleanse her Christian soul without killing her. After all, "[t]he powers of darkness … cannot stand against one holy thing."

The Revolt of the Dead exemplifies something more than a religious battle. It repeatedly draws on racist stereotypes, from an African servant named Bulbo to Trelawney's prediction that Boris "will go completely native and end up with a ring in his nose and a black wife." Africans are described as "savage peoples" and the October 26, 1932, script even suggests an alternate title for the film: *The Revolt of*

Van Sloan). In surviving *Revolt of the Dead* pages, a character named Lord Avon explains, "Gentlemen … We have passed out of the realm of science into that of the <u>Occult</u>." (The line is reminiscent of Van Helsing's "Gentlemen, we are dealing with the … undead.") Renamed Prof. von Haeckelmetz (which became "Hecklemetz"), the same character argues, "Gentlemen, there are things greater than your books … things beyond your Science. There are forces … enormous forces that we do not understand—."

The Revolt of the Dead also bears the influence of George du Maurier's *Trilby* (1894) and its characters Svengali and Trilby. For example, Loogo communicates to Mary hypnotically from afar. In one scene, Logoo

> kept clinching and unclinching his hands in the well-remembered gesture of urgency as if with everything that he had that was either physical or mental, he was trying to force someone else to do something which he resisted doing.

Once under Loogo's evil mind control (which is reminiscent of Murder's in *White Zombie*), the script tells us that Loogo's "awful eyes blazed" inside of Mary's head.

But Browning adds something unique to *The Revolt of the Dead*, something that goes beyond *the Savage*. And then there is Logoo's possession of Mary, which is described not just as demonic, but also as a type of supernatural miscegenation: "His black soul is still in her body." Browning was, alas, no more immune to racism than most other Hollywood filmmakers of the period.

How *The Revolt of the Dead* evolved narratively after October 26, 1932, is unknown. On December 20, 1932, *The Hollywood Reporter* wrote:

> Gouverneur Morris leaves the Universal writing staff, where he made a screen play [*sic*] of *The Invisible Man*, to return to MGM. He will work with Tod Browning on brushing up the script of *Revolt of the Dead* for immediate production.

The fact that MGM considered Browning's project for at least two months during the autumn of 1932 means that Louis B. Mayer and Irving G. Thalberg had not dismissed him as a possible horror movie director in the immediate aftermath of the release of *Freaks*.

Nevertheless, as has happened thousands of times in Hollywood, the project stalled, and never became a movie. *The Revolt of the Dead* was shelved, and what remains of it now is paperwork, not celluloid.

Jean-Luc Godard once said that a "true history of cinema must include all the histories of the films that were never made." Scholars James Fenwick, Kieran Foster and David Eldridge have referred to such unproduced films as "Shadow Cinema." With *The Revolt of the Dead*, we encounter shadow cinema of the most shadowy type, a horror movie that would likely have been too strange, too challenging and too offensive for Classical Hollywood. That it exists in the form of script materials helps us measurably in our pursuit of the "true history" of Tod Browning's cinema.

The Script

The following treatment, from Tod Browning's personal collection,
is the earliest known version of *The Revolt of the Dead*.

THE REVOLT OF THE DEAD

--*-*-*-*-*-*

Two Englishmen   Trelawney and Suffolk constitute an African Outpost

of the British Empire. A guest in their bungalow is a

young Pole, Boris Zwsbisko. Boris is deeply interested in

vodoo. He believes that through vodoo much good could be

done in the world. Except for his morbid curiosity, Boris

is as good a man as you could find.

Trelawney has a sister in London. From her photograph

we judge her to be beautiful and rather sexless. Her letter

tells Trelanny that she is engaged to Dr. Martin.

Back in the jungle is a native village dominated by an

ancient very wise, very wicked witch doctor, Loogo. Boris

spends much of his time with Loogo and is in the old man's

confidence. Loogo does not use drugs or tricks, but hypnotism.

He tells Boris that he can raise the dead if they have not been

dead too long.

Question; How does Boris know that he himself is going to be

raised from the dead?

Boris believes Loogo and wishes to be taught how to raise

the dead himself. Loogo however will tell him anything but

that. Not oftener than once a year, Loogo makes a human

sacrifice to his Gods. The victim must be white.

Having kidnapped the child of a missionary down the

river, Loogo prepares for this event. Boris surprises the

witch Doctor in the act of sacrificing the child and tries

to prevent him. The child's throat is cut with a knife. At

-2-

that moment Trelanny and Suffolk and a dozen black constables
come charging in. Boris has rushed forward to the slain child.
Loogo and the tribesman have withdrawn. It looks as if Boris himself
were the murderer. He denies this with righteous passion but
Loogo and the tribesmen were interrogated but Trelanny, points
accusing fingers at him. Trelanny and Suffolk believe him
guilty beyond a doubt and prepare to execute him on the spot.
Boris makes a **violent speech** in which we shall hope to set
forth with unmistakable clarity the motivation of our story.
That motivation briefly is this. An innocent man is being put
to death. The graveyards of the world are filled with dead
who have been wronged by the living. Boris will come back
from the dead. He will bring back the other dead who have been
wronged and they will crowd the living out of the world. Boris
still protesting is tied against the stockade and filled with
bullets.

That night Trelanny and Suffolk are talking over what Boris
had said. They wonder if it is possible to raise the dead. While
they are talking the dead man appears in the open door of the
bungalow. He does not look at them or threaten them. He seems
to have neither soul nor intelligence. Obviously he is dead and
yet walks like a man. He goes away. When the two Englishman
have pulled themselves together they hurry to Boris's grave.
The body is no longer there.

The dead man does not seem to have any objective but when
the drums of the village begin to beat, he seems to listen and
a flicker of intelligence comes over his face.

The dead man boards his ship and goes to England.

Note: whenever the dead man is at a loss the witch doctor

-3-

by some wirelessing of the drums is able to direct him.
At such times the dead man himself has hypnotic powers. The
dead man makes his headquarters in the subterranean burial vault
of a castle. There have been some recent burials. Boris exhumes
a body and tries to bring it to life but he cannot. Then we hear
the drums and the power to bring the dead to life goes into Boris.
The dead whom he exumes have only this power; to exhume and bring
to life other dead persons.

When Boris finds himself face to face with Miss Trelanny ^{awney}
the sister of the man who had had him executed, the drums beat.
They seem to tell him to exert hypnosis and get her in his power.
He gets her in his power. She and some others become his human
agents. Sylvia Trelanny through no fault of her own does incredibly wicked things. Dr. Martin realizes that there is something horribly wrong with her. She will not or cannot tell him
what the trouble is.

We gather from newspapers, conversations that the dead who
had been brought to life are becoming very numerous. It gets so
that families are afraid to go home after the theatre lest they
find the late Aunt Agatha sitting in the chimney corner. Every
family now realizes that it might have been much much kinder to
its Aunt Agatha.

In a secret place Boris impelled by the drums, compells some
of his human agents to crucify an old miser who had refused to show
them where his gold was hidden. Sylvia comes in just as the
last nail is being driven home. The shock of what she sees tears
her loose from Boris's power. She rushes out on the street and
falls in a dead faint. When she is found and hurried to a
hospital, she bears upon her hands and feet the marks of the
Stigmata. Her forehead looks as if it had been wounded by a

-4-

crown of thorns.

A Question; how are we going to put an end to the power which is menacing the whole world? What is the power? Obviously it is not Boris, it is the witch Doctor. Must we go back to Africa and destroy him? Must we bring him to London? These questions must be answered before we can engineer and climax the hanging scene, and have it all click.

The following handwritten notes are from
Browning's personal collection.

Revolt of the dead

notes

X
36 { Fire place with bag skull
flue flame
Photograph seems to be working
in response

X 41 insert Hocus pocus
B 41 turns his attention toward who
is half conscious — speaks to her softly
about the dead man —
He take the other — without being in
life will walk and find its way
home — carrying disaster Another being dead
Young. him to her who live it and who
(will find that they _____ ___ (_____ more

42 Persuades her — she is thy better and better
bottom 42 I dont mean that I believe in ghosts
but I have had presentiments & to her
my daughter
. She felt a presence so deeply that
the a voice spoke to her and she answered.

44 widow — I have given to her church my
two children — my jewels — and
now they have taken all that I
have left etc
make identity of dead man clear
plant the empty chair.
that chair will always be empty

"wonders why the astral body has
returned

No answer — gives to him
I thought you was a spirit. But
father your hand as cold as ice
feels face heart
Comments

Makes sign of cross on blindly
over father — then turns to God
asks God the meaning. Guide
we loved him. we wanted him
to come back —

Here's a gasp
Don't be frightened
we loved him — we wanted him
back.

Mother must not know

97

Baron Avon a prisoner etc
More together
Weeks later
① Can you feel the presence before it possesses you. Yes. Can you avoid it? No.
② She is completely under him now. When very bad return ... I am always kneeling before him ... than I am myself less ... less often, she has gone from bad to worse

at the end of breaking engagement she breaks down + wants to be dead
"that would do no good"
he would return for a day deaf ...

1 Complete state of possession
to
3 Throw the anticipation to the ...

You have no desire to go to the Church plan?
No, he has possession now. I do them evil things — Soon I shall not wish to condone

Do it with leading questions about hypnosis And plenty of hints from Ambrose

I'll track him down & kill him
(explain that's just will be in
Mary) Is there no way
Yes. This one way
Please don't tell me. I mean I
know — when I'm with him I'll tell him
He goes out
And alchemist tell Doctor
about emancipation & guarantees that
it will work —
He leaves the lovers together he can
fade out. I will meet you. I have
things to prepare

Fade

He explains the emancipation
in foggy hidy place. Also that the
power destroyed the dead will fall over

after alchemist has gone before fade
— Please — Please — don't do anything
— that you can promise —
                        he promises
Sssh   She comes

98

Page 53

Yes

His eyes twitch as if he had a thought
Did you feel that ~~though the the~~
pain was nearly/really gone from away?

Yes

He walks away & then
the ~~Sheta cuts~~ for a clue
Nutzy comes back

55

she shall hide & wait until
his spirit left her and gone back
to him, then we shall kill him

—

But if by chance his spirit will
not leave her body — then we shall
have to drive his spirit from her body
& into his, ~~and that there is still
the body~~

Now

56

the virgin at a for her
but was overcome — she can no longer
bring these pitous wounds upon herself

~~did not leave~~ no leave her

Ⓧ P 58

Prepares to kill

wait till the soul is coming out
of her body & back in his

Then he discharges stone

When she hears that she leaps
to her feet — she recognizes them and
flies into rage.

They hurry toward

Don't use that gun. His soul
is still in her body, with doctor

while they are advancing the spirit
gets control and —

Please wait a little, though I speak
~~in his voice I have~~ If you had
only waited a few moments his soul
would have been completely out of
my body. Even now though I speak
with his voice he has only partial
possession of me. If you harm his
body his soul will remain in mine
forever and ever.

Moves to Professor

This time Professor you blundered.
You have had the only chance that

you will leave and you
leave them dead.

Metz looks with angry
look & says

Perhaps what make you
think so.

I know his thoughts because his
soul is still within me & will
not leave until it is assured — that
it can return to his own body
and be allowed to leave this
place in safety.

Martin Never — I'll fill it full
of lead.

Arthur then I will become
he & we shall be lost to her
power.

Metz.
Promise her to do nothing
rash

I promise.

To him a promise is worth
laugh. Give me the gun he will
only trust me.

No. You one that gun is
in your hands you will kill us
both.

Arthur do you love me. Take

me in your arms. Love me.
Agree to let him go, promise. Give
me the gun.

She puts her arms around
him & looks him a long time
in the eyes.

Mily watches like cat

Arthur releases himself a little
and starts to hand her the
gun —

~~Mily~~

as she to take the gun Mily
knocks it from her hand & throws
her against door —

~~Have you gone mad?~~
~~Leave her alone.~~ Have
you gone mad.

No you the mad one.
One moment more and we would
both be dead men.

Leave her alone!

He parts them
a moment calm — blazing
eyes —

Didn't you hear her say
that the gun had to be in her
possession.

You fool did you for one minute

That it was many speaks
to you. It was the cunning archail
spirit which possessed her & seeks
our destruction —

She gives a scream of
rage like some wild animal
her eyes blazy she makes a
~~swine divine~~ rush for the gun.
~~Again body grapples~~

✱ 60

So it will be with all the
others. death. Has reclaimed its own

The following script, provided by Russell McGee, incorporates all of the changes that Browning desired. A clean and fully typed version of Browning's annotated October 26, 1932, script, it bears the same date.

"THE REVOLT OF THE DEAD"

(or)

"THE REVOLT OF THE SAVAGE"

October 26, 1952.

"THE REVOLT OF THE DEAD"

(or)

"THE REVOLT OF THE SAVAGE"

by

Gouverneur Morris
and
Gerrit Lloyd

From story suggested by
TOD BROWNING

October 26, 1932.

"THE REVOLT OF THE DEAD"
(or)
"THE REVOLT OF THE SAVAGE"

The negro, Bulbo, black as the ace of spades, his eyes shut, lay flat on his back and moved only as much as was necessary to stir the air in the living room of the bungalow. This movement was performed entirely by Bulbo's left foot between whose great toe and the next the cord which passed through the wall of the house and moved the punkah fan was firmly held. Bulbo was not asleep. Unusual sounds from the jungle or the river were instantly registered by various wrinklings of his low forehead and twitching of his ears.

If the punkah moved the air in the living room it did not cool it and George Alfred Trelawney was wet through and the pencil with which he was footing a column of figures slipped in his hand. Trelawney was a long legged Englishman of forty-five but since his teens he had not often seen England. His life's work had been among savage peoples and savage climates. His hair was graying, his skin was tinged with the unmistakable yellow which tells of an unhappy liver. His lean handsomely carved face had a look of temper.

But his expression ought to have been happier because

108

he was now convinced that with the help of young Suffolk and
the Hungarian engineer, Boris Odelosi, he had located and defined
an oil dome of incalculable value.

The living room had a certain picturesqueness due to a
somewhat disordered use of native weapons and fabrics.

From somewhere far off in the jungle there came from
time to time a faint and muffled sound of drums. Sometimes
Trelawney could not be sure that he was hearing drums or the
beating of his own pulses. Since the preceding midnight the thermometer had stood at 103 degrees in the shade.

Three bedrooms opened off the living room. Through a
fourth open door could be seen one corner of a makeshift shower
bath and through a fifth a rectangle of savage landscape in the
midst of which lay rather than flowed a dark river. Into this
rectangle stepped the Reverend Mr. Morrison, the missionary. Mr.
Morrison wore a jacket and trousers of white linen and a pith
helmet. The only thing about his dress to denote his calling was
a gold cross suspended from his neck by a narrow black ribbon.
A stronger note of black was forced by a band of crepe stitched
to his right sleeve. Mr. Morrison was perhaps thirty-five years
old. He had the Zealot's eye, the Zealot's look of self-confidence and a certain mock humility so often associated with the
pulpit.

Trelawney detested missionaries in general and this one
in particular, but the knowledge that this one was in deep trouble
and sorrow brought him to his feet with a pleasant word of welcome
and an extended hand. Mr. Morrison touched the band of crepe on
his arm and said:

"We have decided not to feed any longer on hope. It is

-3-

a month today since our little daughter disappeared. That she
should have survived the dangers and pitfalls of the jungle is
unthinkable. He who has taken her back into His care alone
knows her fate. We console ourself with the belief that it was
swift and painless. Perhaps the quick silent spring of a leopard
and one killing blow of its paw."

"She was a dear little thing," said Trelawney, "I cannot
tell you how profoundly sorry I am for you and your wife."

Stifling a yawn, his hair tousled as if he had been
lying down young Bradley Suffolk emerged from one of the bedrooms.

He shook hands with Mr. Morrison and said that he was
glad to see him.

"And where," asked Mr. Morrison, "is the third musketeer?
Where is Boris?"

"Where he usually is," said Suffolk, "back there in the
village studying native manners and customs, witchcraft, voodoo,
and what have you."

"The first thing we know," said Trelawney, Mr. Boris
Odelosi will go completely native and show up with a ring in his
nose and a black wife."

"Heaven forfend," sighed Mr. Morrison.

"And that," continued Trelawney, "will be a loss to the
British Exploration Company, limited, of a very capable engineer.
That young man has a nose for oil.

"Oil," said Suffolk, "is his business. I wish he would
stop sticking his nose into so many other things that aren't."

"What I really came for," said Mr. Morrison, "is to
thank you for all you have done for us, and all you have tried
to do, in our sorrow and to say goodbye."

-4-

"You're not leaving us!" exclaimed Trelawney.

"For a month only," said Mr. Morrison, "My duty is here and my duty is clear, but Mrs. Morrison is terribly pulled down and I have the hope that a month of sea breezes will bring back the color to her cheeks. Will you kindly convey my respects to Mr. Odelosi when you see him? He and our little baby girl were great friends."

Mr. Morrison turned and really fled from a sudden show of emotion with which he was threatened.

"Did you hear that!" exclaimed Suffolk indignantly, "convey his respects to Mr. Odelosi! He and the little girl were such great friends!"

"Well they were great friends, weren't they," said Trelawney, "he was always playing with her, giving her candy, chocolate."

"Yes," said Suffolk, "to get her confidence and trust. I would bet plenty of money that Mr. Boris Odelosi knows where she is at this minute."

"Just because you happen to hate a man," said Trelawney, "is no reason why you should talk nonsense about him."

"It isn't hatred," said Suffolk, "it's instinct. The man's a rotter. He wouldn't stop at anything to get his way. I believe that he knows where that child is and I believe he took her there."

"What you need," said Trelawney, "is a month's vacation in cold climate. The next thing we know, you will be seeing things."

During all this, while the long punkah fan had been

swinging slowly to and fro. But now it faltered and stopped.
Bulbo had fallen asleep.

Trelawney simply stepped out on the veranda and kicked
him. Bulbo did not open his eyes but once more the foot which
held the punkah cord began to move rhythmically.

The huts of the village had been built in two long
rows. The central space between them served as a street. At
their backs were scrubby plantations; corn, bananas, Indian hemp
and Papaias. Beyond these the tall dark jungle was like a threat.
The houses were shaped like old fashioned beehives. The villagers
usually a boisterous jolly lot were all in the street but there
was no laughing and the only talk was in hushed tones. The villagers seemed to be laboring under a strong but suppressed excitement. It was not yet night but the village was already completely in shadow. One of the huts was much larger than the others.
Out of this presently stepped Boris Odelosi, the Hungarian engineer.
He was a tall man with strong forceful features and there was a
something strange and unforgetable about him. His eyes at once
shone with a fine intelligence and had in them a hint of madness.
He was followed into the open by Loogo, the witch doctor. Loogo
wore none of the insignia of his calling. His face and body were
not painted and his breech clut differed in no way from those
worn by the other men of the tribe. His features were not negroid.
They were thin and sharp. He had a commanding brow. His hair was
snow white. He carried himself and moved with a certain majesty.
Although his body was smooth and firm he looked to be a very
old man.

A complete hush had come over the villagers. The
engineer and the witch doctor with fitting strides walked the
length of the village street in a purposeful way and disappeared into the jungle. The villagers exchanged looks which were at
once knowing and awed.

Having entered the jungle the witch doctor took the
lead. He was careful to step where his feet would leave no track
and the engineer imitated him. They came to a stream and followed it for some distance by wading. They came to an outcrop
of granite rock. Here they left the stream and came at last by
devious windings to a hut so cunningly and secretly hidden that
it could not even have been seen from an airplane. The hut contained two comfortable good-natured looking black women and a
female child. The child wore a little crown of flowers and a
little girdle of flowers. She was a beautiful child. Her hair
was golden and her skin was white. She was not more than three
or four years old.

She ran to Boris Odelosi holding out both her arms. He
swung her lightly from the ground and gave her a smacking kiss.

"Are you happy, Doris?" he asked. "Plenty to eat?
Plenty of toys?"

"Yes," said the child, "But I want to go back to Daddy
and mumsy. I want to go back tonight. Say I can go back tonight.
Promise."

The witch doctor who had been regarding the pair in a
detached way now spoke one word in clear, precise, impeccable
English,

"Promise," he said.

"Alright," said Boris to the child, "I promise."

Boris put the child down and one of the women came forward and took her by the hand. Loogo murmured a word in native and the two women accompanied by the child went out of the hut, but the child looked back at Boris over her shoulder and smiled and he called gayly to her, "See you later."

Loogo's quick eyes caught sight of what had perhaps once been the white child's hair ribbon. He picked this up and dropped it into the remaining embers of the cook fire where it shriveled, blackened, twisted like a snake and became ashes. Then he straightned himself and appeared to listen. He smiled suddenly and said,

"They came."

There came into the hut two tall and magnificent negroes bearing torches. They took positions on opposite sides of the hut and stood motionless. Two women followed them in from the night. The first was a very old woman, withered and shrunken. She carried in her hands a tray skilfully woven from Pandanus leaves. On this tray rested a long straight narrow knife of bright steel. The second woman was young and by African standards, most beautiful. She wore flowers in her hair and a girdle of flowers about her waist. She carried in her hand a cage woven from bamboo splits. In this cage was a white dove.

Loogo took the knife in his right hand, with his left hand he opened the door of the cage and withdrew the dove. For a moment the dove fluttered and then lay still. He opened his hand as if to show that this stillness was not caused by any pressure of his fingers. It was as if the dove had died, then

114

-7-

presently it showed signs of life and began to struggle, to
turn, and get on its feet. But Loogo's hand closed upon its
legs, its tail, and the tips of its wings, imprisoning them. He
held the dove so that his breast was presented to the point of
the knife. Very slowly he transfixed the dove with the knife
so that the point of this stood out between the winged shoulders
then loosening his left hand he lifted the dove, empaled on the
point of the knife, high over his head where it made desperate
efforts to fly, beating frantically with its wings.

Once more Loogo took the dove in his left hand. This
time he withdrew the knife from its breast. There was no blood
upon the knife and when Boris ran his fingers delicately through
the breast feathers of the dove he could not find any wound or
any drop of blood. Loogo returned the knife to the tray from
which he had taken it.

From the night surrounding the hut, came now a sudden
soft, throbbing insistent rhythm of drums. The girl who had
brought the dove to Loogo now advanced with steps which kept
time to the drums and held out her hands for the dove. In each
hand she held one of the bird's wings and one of its legs. The
rhythm of the drums increased in tempo and with it the movements
of the girl's feet and body. As she danced she looked upward
at the dove. The expression on her face was that of a Sadist,
a torturer. Steadily the speed of the drum rhythm increased
and with them the speed of the girl's dancing and it looked now
to Boris as if she were trying to tear the dove apart.

As the dove's breast tore apart and blood flowed, the
girl's dancing went into a kind of frenzy. The blood ran down

her arms and dropped on her upturned face. Suddenly the music
of the drums came to a full stop and so also the dancing of the
girl. She bent forward, lower and lower until the dove was above
the knife. Blood fell upon the knife. Almost it seemed as if
the dove were a sponge which the girl was wringing. When the knife
had been sanctified with the blood of the dove, the drums again
began to beat, this time with an incredible agitation and fury.
The girl kept time with her feet and body, her face now like that
of a maniac, upturned to the bleeding, mangled dove. The dance
came to a sudden, and to Boris, an unexpected end. The girl gave
one long piercing scream and fell to the floor in convulsions.

The drums had stopped beating. There was complete
silence. Everything was still except the shuddering, convulsed
body of the dancer. When Loogo brought the palms of his hands
smartly together they made a sound as sharp and startling as a
pistol shot.

Two women came in out of the night, mastered the frantic
struggles of the dancer and carried her away. Loogo dismissed the
torch bearers with a curt gesture. He and Boris and the woman
who had brought the knife were alone in the hut. Loogo examined
the knife to see if it had been well blooded. In returning it to
the tray he said solemnly:

"In hoc signo vincimus."

"By jove!" said Boris, "Latin!"

The woman turned and went out of the hut.

"Is there any language that you _don't_ speak," asked
Boris.

"Not any," said Loogo.

"That is the most amazing thing about you. You have never been out of this fever jungle and yet you can speak all the polite languages under the sun."

"My astral body," said Loogo, "has been a great traveller. It has been in Germany, France, England, America often. I have a quick ear."

"Will my astral body be able to go on journeys?" asked Boris.

"Of course," said Loogo, "and even now with my help you could travel to Budapest and see your Father and your Mother. Would you like that?"

"I am a little homesick for them," said Boris simply.

"Then lie down on this mat," said Loogo.

Boris lay down on the mat and Loogo squatting beside him looked him fixedly in the eyes and made quick passes over his cheeks and temples.

Boris' eyes closed, his entire body stiffened convulsively, and then relaxed. A dead man could not have seemed more still. The witch doctor smiled. It was the smile of an old man who is giving pleasure to a child.

Odelosi's parents, his younger brother Paul and his two sisters were at dinner. It was a warm night and the French windows along one side of the room were open.

Suddenly, Madame Odelosi turned in her chair with extended arms and a happy look on her face. "Boris," she said, "my darling."

But there was no Boris standing beside her. Odelosi and his son were on their feet. The older man's forehead was beaded with sudden sweat. The eyes of the two sisters were wide with amazement.

"Where is Boris!" exclaimed the mother, "he was here. He called me 'motherkin'. He laid his cheek against mine. Boris where are you hiding?"

Her expression had changed to one of perplexity and anxiety.

"Did none of you see him?" she asked.

"I didn't see him," said her husband, "but I felt that he was in the room.

"So did I", so did I," said the daughters.

"I know that he was in the room," said Paul.

The family rushed on to the balcony on which the French windows opened but there was no one there, only the night set thickly with lights.

Loogo continued to smile.

"You have traveled," he said, "you have seen your father and your mother."

He made passes over the cheeks and temples of the Hungarian. A look of wonder came over Boris' face and his eyes opened.

"I saw them," he said, "and I wanted to stay a long time. My Father looks very old, but I couldn't stay."

He got to his feet and shook himself. He was now completely out of the trance into which he had been thrown.

"Loogo," said Boris, "with the knowledge and power that your people have had for thousands of years, how is it possible for you to be driven back by the white man's civilization?'

118

"There are many reasons," said Loogo, "Cannon, warships, airplanes, whiskey and greed."

"But", said Boris, "your power, the power of the occult is so much more wonderful than science. You begin where science leaves off. If you wish to know what is going on in London or New York, you have only to go and see for yourself and nobody can see you or hurt you. It is incredible that science should have defeated the occult and driven it to the wall."

"But," said Loogo, "the battle is not finished. Science has not defeated the occult. Not yet. Come."

They went out into the night and retraced their steps to the village. By one of the outlying huts, Loogo haulted.

"I am going to show you something," he said, "that science can not do."

They approached the windows of the hut which stood open and looked in. The interior was illumined by a small fire and by candle nuts set on iron spikes. Over the fire was suspended an iron pot and a comely negress was stirring its contents. Two bright eyed children watched this operation with interest.

On the edge of a cot bed, looking and not looking, dumb, sightless, without thought, sat a dead man. Garlands of withered flowers hung about his neck and loins. He made no motion of any kind.

"A Zombie," whispered Boris.

The upper lip of the witch doctor curled scornfully.

"A Zombie," he said, "is only a wretched man who has been drugged. That man is a dead man who has come back.

"Horrible," said Boris with a shudder.

119

-12-

"Not to us," said Loogo, "We are used to them.
The woman wanted her husband back so I gave him to her. I cannot
give him back his soul, but I can lend him my own soul. Would
you like to see that?"

They went into the hut and after he had greeted the
woman, Loogo laid himself down on the cot on the edge of which
the dead man was sitting. It could be seen by the strained muscles of Loogo's face and the blazing concentration of his eyes
that he was making some tremendous effort of the will. Boris
watched the eyes of the witch doctor. For a time they seemed to
be on fire. Slowly the fire in them began to die. Boris looked
at the dead eyes of the dead man. Light was coming into them.
They moved in their sockets. The dead man's brows twitched.
The dead man opened his mouth and spoke in the voice of the
witch doctor.

"You see," the voice said, "he talks English just as
well as I do."

The dead man turned to the woman and still with Loogo's
voice but now in the native tongue, spoke to her and seemed to
be saying kind and appreciative things. He spoke also to the
children, addressing them by their names and they ventured a step
or two in his direction, but then as quickly as the light had
come into the dead man's eyes, it went out of them and Loogo's
eyes which had seemed for a time like those of a dead man, became
once more bright with the fire of his intelligence. The witch
doctor got up from the bed.

"If they loved each other," asked Boris, "why didn't he
embrace her and kiss her when he had the chance?"

"It was not his soul that was in him," said Loogo,

120

-13-

"But mine, and my soul does not happen to wish for the embraces of this particular woman."

"And do your people," asked Boris, "really want to have
their dead with them?"

"Yes," said the old man, "all those who love their departed want them."

"In civilization," said Boris, "there is no place for
the dead. If the dead were to return to those who love them, it
would drive them insane to have them sitting around like this."

"It would do what?" asked Loogo quickly.

"Drive them insane," said Boris, "Drive them mad."

The old man looked like someone who has been suddenly
struck with a tremendous thought. He looked younger. He held
himself more erect.

"It would drive them mad," he said.

They went out into the night. The hut to which the
dead man had returned was a little removed from the village.
There was a piece of black forest between. The moon which had
risen, made gleaming high-lights on the leaves and trunks of trees.
Through the trees, moving listlessly and without purpose, came a
little procession of five dead men who had come back. Boris and
the witch doctor drew a little to one side while the dead men
passed by.

"More of them," said Boris.

The old man seemed to be laboring under a great excitement. He pushed Boris ahead of him as if very eager now to get
back to his own house and he exclaimed in a strong voice as they
hurried on:

"There will be more of them, hundreds of them, thousands

of them."

The village street was crowded with men, women and
children, in a suppressed state of excitement. The drums throbbed
with strong insistence, many of the villages had painted their
faces and bodies with horrible designs. Many wore head dresses
of nodding Ostrich feathers. Some had concealed their faces
behind hideous masks. The warriors carried shields of rhinocerous
and hippopotamus hide and clusters of throwing and stabbing spears.
As Boris and Loogo began to pass through this crowd toward the
house that was bigger than the other houses, the tempo and the
strength of the drums increased and the crowd kept time with a
rhythmic stamping of the feet. Eyes and teeth gleamed. Some of
the younger people shuddered as if they were cold. Some of the
older women rocked slowly on their feet and made a sound of low
moaning. At the entrance to his house, Loogo paused for a moment
and looked up at the moon dripping with light. Then he passed
into the house, followed by Boris. Against the walls of the house,
hung all the regalia and paraphernalia of a great witch doctor.
Feather cloaks and capes of great beauty, hideous masks. Ranged
along the walls like whitewashed stones in gardens, were skulls
of enemies who had been killed in battle. Loogo took from the wall
a cloak of black and white feathers. The white feathers made
between the shoulders the design of a huge skull. But the rhythm
of the drums and excitement in the street without, were too strong
to be resisted, and Boris went back to the door and looked out.
The excitement of the people like the tempo of the drums was in
a steady crescendo. Boris was almost unnerved by the sheer savage-
ness of it. When his eyes once more returned to the witch doctor,

this one, by a swift and sure use of pigments and regalia
had been transformed into a thing of majesty and horror toward
which Boris seemed to be drawn by some unseen force. Loogo
made a curt imperious gesture and Boris knew that he had been
commanded to take off his tunic. This done and bare to the
waist he faced the witch doctor and this one painting swiftly,
traced on the dazzling white hairless breast of the young man,
the symbol of death, a black skull.

Then they went out into the street. The villagers
had formed themselves into two long lines. As the witch doctor
and the Hungarian passed between these, the lines closed in behind them and the whole village moved toward the jungle, in a
well ordered procession of nodding plumes and shaking spears.
The beating of the drums rose almost to a frenzy as they disappeared into the jungle.

In the midst of dark and still waters from which grew
a forest of the immense buttressed melancholy trees there was a
long and narrow turtleback of dry land. Here the tribe knelt
like worshippers in a cathedral, before a high altar that was
built with human skulls.

At   strategic points, torches had been stuck in the
ground. On the altar itself was something that burned with a
blue flame. Drums spoke to each other in muffled whispers
but there was always rhythm and from time to time this rhythm
mysteriously changed. The bodies of those who knelt swayed to
the rhythm of the drums. Plumed heads were bent. Hands were
crossed upon breasts. Before the high altar, with his back to
what we may perhaps call his congregation, stood the witch

doctor. He stood without motion. His face was turned upward
to the blue flame on the altar. The focus of the entire scene
was, however, the skull embroidered with white feathers
between the shoulders of his black cloak.

Boris was not in evidence. Between the witch doctor
and those who knelt in the first row was an open space. In this
space some tens of doves cooed and hunted for seeds. Among
the doves, three from each side, came six little girls. They
were so young that even in that luxuriant climate their breasts
had not yet begun to swell. They were garlanded with lovely
flowers. Their little black faces were very serious and solemn.
They came dancing with light and delicate steps. They were so
bright in the night, their eyes so shining, that they resembled
fire-flys.

The witch doctor turned and faced them. He made an upward gesture with his right hand and for a few moments the drums
roared fortissimo.

Some of the drums were grouped. Some were solitary.
Some were great. Some were small. Some were no more than a
slotted cylinder of wood. Each drum had a percussive voice peculiar
to itself. Sometimes the drums became a chorus. Sometimes one
little drum spoke to a great drum and was answered. Drums which
were near together seemed to speak in whispers. Those which
were far apart spoke, each from its dark place, loud and clear.
Hear and there, caught in the light of a torch and turned upward
and illumined by the full moon could be seen the face of a drummer.
For the most part these drummers were strong men. They gleamed
with sweat and although they had been drumming almost without
cessation for hours and hours, they showed no signs

of exhaustion. The expression on these faces varied with the rhythm of the moment. At times there was sweetness and tranquility. At times frank savage excitement, but sometimes it seemed as if they were experienceing some sort of monstrous delight.

The drums, having roared in unison, became silent. Again the witch doctor lifted his right hand and the drums broke into a light syncopation that had about it a something innocent and gay. To these measures the six little girls danced in front of the altar.

Out of the darkness, at the rear of the worshippers, came Boris, his snow-white back in strong contrast to the dark brown and black bodies of those who swayed before the altar. Boris was carrying something in his arms, but only the witch doctor who faced him could see what this was. As Boris moved slowly forward toward the witch doctor and the altar of skulls, the drum beats smote the air more thicklyand more loudly until almost it seemed as if many lions were roaring.

Boris Odelosi knelt before the high priest and this one took from his extended arms the little child of the missionary. As he turned to lay her on the altar, it could be seen that she was so frightened that she could not even scream. From the left side of the altar came the old woman with the matted tray of Pandanus leaves, upon which lay the knife, stained with the pure blood of the dove. It seemed as if the drums and the congregation had gone demoniac, but when the witch doctor took up the knife in his hand and held it aloft so that it pointed at the moon, the

-18-

drums became silent. The wild bodies motionless as if frozen.

In that silence only the children moved and there could be heard the light tappings of their little feet. They seemed to be dancing a series of little geometric figures that became one thing and then dissolved into another. As they danced, they lifted their clear shrill voices in a kind of chant. Their voices broke upon the silence like the voices of tree-frogs. Having completed their evolutions three of the little girls danced off into the night at one end of the altar and three into the night at the other.

The child had been laid on the high altar of skulls, just below the blue flame. But the savage worshippers could no longer see her because of the bodies of the high priest, and of Boris who had risen to his feet. Boris and the witch doctor drew closer to the child and it could be sensed that the latter was going to do some awful thing with the knife.

A scream, too piercing, too pitiable, too shot with terror to be described in words, broke the silence. Then, once more the drums went into action. From a steady beating in groups of six long beats, followed by two short ones, there developed swiftly and with a crescendo that became tremendous rhythms too complicated and exciting for a white ear to follow.

It is difficult to find words with which to describe what followed. The congregation had come to their feet and it seemed as if sanity had departed from them altogether. They danced and contorted their bodies with the utmost conceivable demonstrations of violence and they screamed at the tops of their lungs.

-19-

The sound of a drum even when it is tapped lightly,
carries far. When a well trained African band goes mad as on
the present occasion, the sound carries for miles and miles.
The savages beat upon the ground with their foreheads and the
palms of their hands. So also here and there in the dark forest,
in far off and isolated dwellings, wild people knew the meaning
of the drumming and moaned and screamed with excitement and
knelt and pounded the floor with their heads and hands. ~~So also
Bulbo, who had been ordered to the punkah rope because the night
was very hot, hearing those drums became half mad with excitement
and knelt and pounded the floor with their heads and hands.~~ So
also Bulbo, who had been ordered to the punkah rope because the
night was very hot, hearing those drums became half made with
excitement, dropped the punkah rope and beat upon the floor of the
veranda with his hands and his head.

Whenever Trelawney had been on the point of falling
asleep, the drums had prevented. What he thought and what he
occasionally said about black people in general and black drumming
in particular was not of an edifying nature. Indeed some of his
explosions were not fit to print. Suffolk, always in an angry
mood these days, a young man who had been completely "gotten" by
the climate, had not even attempted to sleep. The little steamer
that came up the river once a month and was even now tied at the
wharf, had brought a whole bag full of letters, magazines and
newspapers. A letter from his sister, Mary, whom he loved
dearly, had given him surprise, pleasure and annoyance. It took
very little to annoy him. Under separate cover she had sent him
a copy of her latest photograph. He propped this against a pile

of books on the table in front of him and as he looked at it
his face softened. She was very beautiful, a tender lovely
English face, like a flower. He thought her very lovely and
in the same moment thought that if those drums didn't stop
that mad rhythm, he would go mad. On the instant, each pore
in his body opened wide and he went into a sudden drenching
sweat and then he really did go mad for he saw that the punkah
had stopped swinging. He rushed out on the veranda to find the
frenzied Bulbo beating the veranda floor with his head and hands.
He kicked him savagely into attention.

"What are they doing?" he cried, "What are these drums
saying?"

Bulbo shook his head repeatedly.

"Don't tell me you don't know, you black dog. I am
going to know what <u>you</u> know if I have to choke it out of you."
And he began to choke the negro with hands that in the frenzy of
his anger, were strong as steel. The negro was the bigger and
the stronger man of the two but he was not able to free himself.
His eyes began to glaze over, he felt the approach of death and
somehow managed to signify that he was now willing to tell.
Suffolk freed the man's throat and Bulbo, after he had swallowed
hard two or three times, said:

"Witch doctor make sacrifice."

"It is not a goat this time," said Suffolk. "They don't
make that much noise for a goat. Is this a human sacrifice? Is it
a man?"

Bulbo shook his head.

"A woman?"

Again Bulbo shook his head.

"A child?"

This time Bulbo bowed his head as if he were terribly ashamed.

"I knew it," cried Suffolk, "Boris, that dirty monster! So help me, I'll get him!"

He rushed back into the bungalow and took his automatic from a drawer in the writing table. At that moment Trelawney, curious about the disturbance on the verandah and the high tones of Suffolk, came out of his bedroom.

"Hey! Hey!," he said, "what are you going to do with that?"

"They are sacrificing a child," said Suffolk, "And I know what child. Boris has let them do it. I knew it was going to happen. He kidnapped her. I am going to kill him."

"Oh, no you arn't," said Trelawney cooly, and with a sudden motion, quick as a snake striking, he snatched the automatic from the younger man's hand.

"You are not going to kill him for three good reasons," he said, "the first is that if you went among those savages in their present mood, they would tear you to pieces; the second reason is that you have no proof of any kind against Boris, and the third is that you are in my employ and subject to my orders and I order you to stop making a damn fool of yourself.

Perceiving that Suffolk was beginning to cool down, Trelawney patted him affectionately onthe shoulders and changed the subject.

At that moment, the frenzy of the drums ended and was

followed by a deathlike silence. This, in turn, was broken by the croaking of frogs and the shrill cry of a night bird.

But the swamps surrounding the island on which the altar of skulls had been built, teemed with frogs and the voices of these rose in great choruses and creakings, now hoarse and low, now shrill, and now strong clarion and clear, almost like the notes of a braying jackass. There could be heard also the varied cries of many birds.

Of those who had witnessed the sacrificing of the missionary's child, only Boris and Loogo remained. Into a bowl which contained a dark liquid, blood perhaps, Loogo dipped the fore-finger of his right hand and occasionally refreshing his supply of pigment, enclosed the black skull which he had already painted on the breast of Boris with a broad dark circle.

Trelawney had gone back to bed to make another try for sleep and Suffolk considerably calmer had finished going through his mail. The photograph of his sister caught his eye, and he spoke to it.

"The idea!" he exclaimed, "you blithering little idiot! I could break your damn neck for suggesting such a thing."

From his bedroom came the angry voice of Trelawney.

"Can't you let a man sleep!" he exclaimed. "Who are you talking to now?"

"I'm talking to my damned fool sister, if you want to know," shouted Suffolk, once more ready to fly off the handle.

Trelawney came out of the bedroom, drew near the table, picked up the photograph of Mary Suffolk, and looked at it.

"Is this your sister?" he asked.

130

"Yes," said Suffolk, "but she is a damned little
fool and if she had been here when I read her letter, I'd have
just about wrung her neck."

"No, really," said Trelawney, "Whatever has the pretty
creature been and gone and done?"

"Well, first of all," said Suffolk, "She has engaged
herself to marry Dr. Martin, The Dr. Martin."

"Well," said Trelawney, "Isn't that rather top-hole?"

"Righto," said Suffolk, "and then the blithering little
idiot proposes to come here to this lousy fever-hole to spend
her honeymoon.

"That wouldn't be a good idea, would it!" said Trelawney,
"Nothing fades so quickly in a climate like this as an English
rose."

He glanced at his wrist-watch.

"I've done you an injustice," he said, "I seem to have
slept for two hours, and that can only mean that for that unprecedented length of time, you have managed to keep your mouth
shut."

"What time is it?" asked Suffolk.

"Two o'clock," said Trelawney.

"I think," said Suffolk, "that I'll do a little turning
in myself."

But he did not at once do this. The sound of distant
steps had caught his ear. He turned his head a little, the better
to listen.

"There is Boris now," he said.

The steps crunching on the gravel path could now be

131

heard more clearly, but they were not even nor alike. One made a firm crisp sound and the other a shuffling sound. This difference was more clearly pronounced when the steps had mounted the veranda stair and moved along the veranda toward the door of the living room.

The two Englishmen started as if they had been guilty of something and Boris Odelosi entered the room. The emotions of the night had effected him profoundly. There was to begin with the feeling that new and unheard of powers had been born in him. In the second place he felt so fatigued and washed out that he had no wish to exercise those powers. He wished of all things to fling himself down on a bed and sleep. He had not expected to find the Englishmen awake. He was annoyed, and still more so when Suffolk pointed an accusing finger at him and said:

"I know what you have done. Bulbo told me and you are not going to get away with it."

The Hungarian had a kind of liking for Suffolk, but no especial respect for his mental and physical powers. If there was going to be a scene he did not wish to be part of it.

"Suppose," he said, "we discuss all that after breakfast. I am tired and if you don't mind _too_ much, I am going to get some sleep."

He moved toward the door of his bedroom, but Suffolk intervened. Trelawney, who did not share the younger man's passions and prejudices,was frankly bored.

"You'd better get some sleep yourself," he said to Suffolk, "and if you don't happen to wake up for a month, nobody would be the worse for it."

It was as if Suffolk had not heard. His eyes were trying to tear the truth from those of Boris'.

"You are beginning to be offensive," said this one. The phrase and the contemptuous tone in which it was uttered were too much for Suffolk. He clenched his fists and with the curious lack of the knowledge of how to use them, which, like the inability to swim, is born in the average white man, made a furious swinging lead with his right. The Hungarian ducked under this without hurrying too much and as he did so, felt his temper rise. Perceiving that the failure of the Englishman to land his swing had drawn him off his balance and made of his right jaw an inviting target, the temptation to hit proved irresistible. Boris had long shapely heavy hands. His punch was like the kick of a mule. When Suffolk came to and got to his knees, he had only an indistinct knowledge of what had happened, but in his heart the unreasoning hate still burned. He got to his feet and staggered to the writing table. He seemed to lean on this for support like a drunken man; but as events almost instantly proved, his mind had cleared and reasoned and reached a definite and logical conclusion. He conceded that physically he was no match for Boris, but the automatic which Trelawney had put back in its drawer would swing the balance of power the other way. The Hungarian in the meanwhile had shrugged his shoulders and turned to Trelawney.

"I am sorry," he said.

Suffolk had taken the automatic from the drawer and moved the safety bolt from safe to ready.

Boris turned and received a 45 caliber nickel-coated bullet in the exact center of his heart. If that heart had been

133

-26-

protected by an inch of armor plate, the mere impact of the
bullet would have knocked him down.

Trelawney knelt at once by the fallen man and in an
instant of time perceived that he was stone dead. He remained
calm.

"How," he said coldly to Suffolk, "do you propose to
square yourself with the autorities?"

Suffolk was a weak man. In pulling the trigger of the
automatic, he had thought of himself as something noble and just,
the young St. Michael overthrowing Lucifer. He no longer felt
noble. He knew that in a moment or two he would be actively sick
at his stomach and he shook with strongly pronounced jerking
shakings like a man who has palsy; but without any knowledge of
what he was doing, without any volition but that of instinct to
do it, he returned the automatic to its accustomed drawer and
shut this with a haste that amounted to violence.

There was a moment in which, if either of the Englishmen
had happened to be looking in that direction, the face of Bulbo,
agog with fright and horror, might have been seen in the dark
rectangle of the window.

"The best that you can hope for," said Trelawney, "if
the law takes its course, is life imprisonment and if I were to
go into the witness box and tell of the absolutely unprovoked and
hideous thing that I have seen you do, you would hang."

"I say," said Suffolk, his hands at his throat, "I say,
don't talk that way. Great God, man, can't you do something!
Can't you get me out of this? I tell you I can't go to prison.
I'd sooner kill myself."

"Well," said Trelawney quietly, and if a stone could speak, it would have just such a voice, "there ought to be at least eight more cartridges in that pistol of yours and one of them, if you aim right and don't flinch ought to do the trick."

But Suffolk's threat to take his own life had no more meaning than the usual talk of suicide. He did instead a thing far more shocking. He burst into tears and dropped to his knees at Trelawney's feet and made the sounds, mostly inarticulate, of a little child that is in horrible trouble.

"Pull yourself together," said Trelawney, still cold as ice. If questions are asked, Boris, in a delirium of malaria, shot himself. If no questions are asked he simply disappeared. If you don't pull yourself together at once I shall lose my temper and break every bone in your body. Going to be sick, are you? Better take yourself out beyond the veranda rail."

While Suffolk was at the business of being sick over the veranda rail Trelawny straightened the arms and legs of the dead man and brought from behind the curtain in a corner of the room two of the long-handled shovels which are used for digging post holes.

They dug the grave behind some hibiscus bushes in a corner of the compound. The moon now low in the heavens watched the burial from the beginning to the end. The frogs in the river and swamps made sounds which were neither dolorous nor merry. The moon watched all the time. She saw the dead man half carried and half dragged from the bungalow to the appointed spot. She saw the whole digging of the shallow grave. She would have given Trelawney most of the credit for the celerity of the accomplishment, for every now and then Suffolk had to drop his shovel and be sick. She saw them lower the body of Boris Odelosi into the grave. She saw Trelawney cross his hands upon his breast, but it is doubtful if she heard his attempts to remember some of the tremendous phrases from the service which the Church of England prescribes for the burial of the dead.

"I am the resurrection and the life'," he said, and after getting all mixed up in the part in which the grave is asked to describe the exact location of its victory and death is denied its sting, he recalled only that "Man that is born of woman hath but a little time to live."

The moon saw the filling in of the grave and the puncti-lious effort of the two Englishmen to make the freshly stirred earth look no different from the hard and trampled earth sur-rounding it. But from a post behind the hibiscus bushes, the negro Bulbo, looked on only long enough to fix the exact location of the grave in his rudimentary mind. He then stole away, silent as a shadow until he had made a safe offing. Then he broke into the long strided swift graceful and contained gait of the born runner. As straightly as the needle heads for the magnetic pole, so straightly did Bulbo steer for the house of the medicine man.

The Englishmen returned to the bungalow and Trelawney shot half a grain of morphine into the upper arm of the hysterical Suffolk. The morphine quieted Suffolk's nerves a little but did not make him sleepy. He walked the length of the room again and again. Trelawney had no thought of sleep either. He sat in the easiest of the chairs and smoked innumerable cigarettes.

Once more, with only the light of the low hanging moon and the blue fire, Loogo, the witch doctor knelt before the altar of skulls.

The tribe, with the exception of one torch bearer who stood beside the witch doctor and the dancing girl who knelt near him and facing him, had departed. Between them, face upward, lay the body of Boris Odelosi. The face and hands and the crumpled white suit were stained with earth. The witch doctor spoke to the dancing girl in quick urgent tones and she in similar tones seemed to speak to the dead man. Presently, however, she unbuttoned the dead man's tunic and laid her left hand over his heart. She laid her right hand over her own heart. At this the witch doctor began to clinch and unclinch his hands. As he clinched them he brought them forward and inward in a gesture of powerful urgency. So you may have seen a man at the race track making an unconscious effort to encourage the horse, upon which he had placed his money, to greater exertions, to the one last desperate necessary burst of speed. Upon the knitted brows of the commanding face of the witch doctor was an expression of concentration so powerful that it amounted to torment. He was urging the warm vital current which controls locomotion to pass from the body of the dancing girl into that of the dead man. But the dead man lay still and his wide-open eyes were glazed and dead.

The dancing girl leaned closer and closer to the body. She leaned until the back of her right hand, which covered her own heart, touched the back of the left hand which covered the dead heart of Boris. During this ceremony the witch doctor seemed to redouble in concentration and urgency. But the dead man continued to lie still and dead.

The witch doctor spoke an order in native to the torch
bearer and this one laid down the torch at the side of the body
so that the face which had been brightly lighted was now in
shadow. Then once more the witch doctor urged the dead man to
come back.

It could be seen that something was beginning to happen
in the shadow. A kind of fluttering and a struggling. The
torch bearer lifted the torch from the ground and it could be
seen that the dead body was struggling upward into a sitting
position. The witch doctor rose and helped the dead man to his
feet.

"Easy, easy," he said, "you will be stronger in a
minute."

The eyes of the dead man were without expression or
objective. They were nothing but dead eyes. In the briefest
glance it could be seen that no brain was functioning in the
dead head. But the thing moved. It was able presently to stand
by itself. It tried out its waxing strength. It took a falter-
ing step or two. The fingers of the medicine man lightly held
and steadied these efforts by the left elbow. Presently the
corpse was walking alone. It moved off all by itself into a
night which became darker and darker as the moon dropped down
behind the rim of the world.

The witch doctor, his face streaming with sweat and
furrowed with pain, turned and made one last deep obeisance
before the high altar of skulls. Then he looked at the blue fire
and the fire went out as if it had been quenched by sudden rain.
Then the medicine man turned and hurried off into the night,

- 31 -

preceeded by the torch bearer and followed by the girl.

Suffolk was still pacing the length of the room, up and down, up and down. The cigarette stubs in Trelawney's ash tray were now so congested that he rose and pitched them into the waste paper basket. The sound of the cigarette stubs hitting smartly against crisp paper and wicker-work, startled Suffolk like sudden drums. He turned quickly. His mouth twisted side-wise like that of a cornered rat.

But at that moment there could be heard a sound of distant steps that approached through the night. One foot seemed to step crisply and firmly. The other made a shuffling sound. The faces of the two listening Englishmen became ash-white with fear and horror. The familiar steps drew nearer and nearer. Sharp and shuffling, they mounted the veranda stair. Sharp and shuffling they came along the veranda floor and a moment later all that was left of Boris Odelosi, the dead eyes, the crumpled white suit stained with earth, walked into the room. The room smelled of the grave. Just under the left breast a brown smear of dried blood surrounded a black puncture and showed how the dead man had come by his death.

Suffolk screamed like a woman. Trelawney clutched at his heart. For a crumb of time it had stopped beating. Between two of the bedroom doors was a low couch or day bed. The dead man walked slowly to this couch and sat down on it.

Now Suffolk himself had killed the man who sat on the couch. He had shot him clean through the heart. He had helped to bury that man and he had felt that he stiffened and grew cold. Well, somehow the dead man had gotten out of the grave and had come back. He was smeared with the earth in which he had been buried. He smelled of it. And there was the bloody hole that had been drilled through his heart.

Suffolk could bear no more. He went completely off his head, and then in a frenzy rushed out into the black night.

Trelawney, that strong man, was now also in a state of nerves and terror which bordered on collapse. He, too, rushed out into the night. But the direction in which Trelawney fled was one which he would hardly have chosen if there had been in him in those moments any power of choice. The thing to do was to get away. He crashed through the hibiscus bushes in the corner of the compound and almost fell into the grave, now empty, which he had helped to dig. Then he, too, screamed and cleared presently the five-foot stockade of the compound as lightly and easily as if he had been a young antelope.

An amused expression on his face, Loogo, the witch doctor, walked quietly into the living room of the bungalow. He was dressed in the two-piece suit of white duck affected by Englishmen in the tropics. He wore a white pith helmet on his head and black patent leather shoes on his feet. He was as spruce and neat as a new pin. He carried a cowhide valise. His glance did not linger long on the dead man. He put down the valise. He passed the length of the room, entered the bathroom and turned on the shower. Then he came back to the dead man and once more making a gesture of urgency with his clenched hands, but a gesture which no longer had in it any appearance of undue energy, he told him to get up. Then as the corpse rose to its feet, he addressed it in the cheerful crisp tones of a servant who is at once familiar and respectful.

"Have to clean you up a little, sir," he said.
"Better get your clothes off, sir."

The dead man unbuttoned his tunic and took if off.
Then he moved toward the bathroom. Loogo amused himself by
glancing through the opened letters with which Suffolk had
littered the writing table. But only the one from the young
man's sister held his interest from the beginning to the end.
The photograph of her also interested him. Looking at it seemed
to have the effect of drying his lips for he repeatedly wetted
them with the tip of his tongue, and a beast look came into his
eyes.

The witch doctor wrapped the letter about the photograph and opening his valise slipped them inside.

But when he followed the dead body of Boris Odelosi,
now in immaculate tropic white, up the gang-plank of the little
river steamer, he had an extra valise, his dress-suit case and
some steamer rugs in a shawl strap.

Near the head of the gang-plank stood the boat's
purser leaning on the rail. Loogo stopped and addressed him.

"When do we sail?" he asked.

"In twenty minutes," said the purser.

"Shall we be in time," asked Loogo, "to make connections
with the mail steamer for England?"

"Time and to spare," said the purser.

A yellow fog had come over the Thames River from the
sea and invaded the great city of London. It was a fog of
varying densities. It varied from light mist to a watery opague-
ness. You could see for instance the dome of St. Paul Cathedral,
but not the body of the church. Cleopatra's Needle was visible.
The tower of London was not. About the Sackville Club the fog
was so dense that the members could not see out of the windows.
And an American caught in such a fog could not have been stopped
from talking about it. To an Englishman it was, however, only a
very usual climatic condition. Mortimer Johnson stood in front
of the coal fire in the club library and warmed his back and read
a newspaper. There were several other readers in the room.

On the chimney breast above Mr. Johnson's head was a
bronze plaque in which was carved the latin word for silence. In
spite of this warning Mr. Johnson was so interested and intrigued
by an item which had caught his eye that he could not refrain from
expressing these feelings out loud.

"By jove!" he said, "Now I say! Now, really!"

A fragile old gentleman put down his own newspaper and
joined Mr. Johnson in front of the fireplace.

"Did you see this bit, sir?" asked Mr. Johnson, and
before the old man could answer, two other members impelled by
curiosity came forward.

"It is the first time it has ever happened in history,"
said Mr. Johnson.

"The first time that what has even happened?" asked
the old man.

"The first time that a shark has followed a ship all

the way across the ocean and this time it wasn't only one shark.
It was hundreds of sharks, thousands of them. The Londonerry,
sailing from Wamba on the west coast of Africa docked this
morning at the King George dock. Her captain reports that he had
no sooner made his offing and rung for full speed ahead when
sharks began to appear in the wake of the vessel. They followed
him clear to the mouth of the Thames and half way up the river."

"There must have been a dead man on board," said the
old man, "Sailors believe that when there is a dead man on a
ship, sharks follow that ship in the hope that the dead man will
be thrown over to them."

"That's the funny part of it," interrupted Johnson,
excitedly. "That's just what the captain said - 'as if there
were a corpse aboard.'"

If the club members had happened to be in a certain
distant part of London, they might have seen going through a
narrow street in which mist drifted, the dead body of Boris
Odelosi followed at a respectful distance by its servant, Loogo,
the witch doctor.

The house in which the beautiful Mary Suffolk lived
with her father and mother and thought often, with deep interest
and affection of her brother over the seas in dark Africa, was
pure Adams, except that there had been added certain deeper
and softer pieces of modern furniture for the sake of comfort.
The mantelpiece was of a soft yellow marble into which had been
let medallions in blue and white, made by the famous Mr. Wedgewood
after classic designs by the equally famous Mr. Flaxman.

By the afternoon post, Mary had received a letter from

brother which had greatly disturbed her. She had read it over a number of times and had discussed its contents with both her parents and now she had been reading it to her fiancé, Dr. Arthur Martin, who had dropped in on his way home from the hospital. Dr. Martin, a tall, strong, smooth-shaven, immaculate-ly-tailored man of forty, now held the letter in his hands. He had been reasoning with her and trying to calm her.

"But," she said, "It's such a strange, mad letter. It isn't in the least like my brother."

"The passage," said Dr. Martin, "in which he forbids his charming sister to spend her honeymoon in a fever swamp is clear enough."

"Yes," said the girl, "But there are passages which I don't understand at all. What does he mean about 'a country where the dead come back to life and walk the earth as living dead things'?"

Dr. Martin smiled in a cool quizzical way. "I am sure I don't know," he said.

"I have felt so queer since the letter came," said she. "I feel as if something were trying to invade my personality and destroy its integrity, and I am so worried about Jeffrey. Darling, you don't think, you don't think that by any chance my poor brother is going - mad?"

The doctor opened his arms and she went into them like a homing pigeon.

"Of course, I don't," he said, "And you must stop feeling queer."

He kissed her on the mouth with great sweetness and tenderness.

144

-37-

"Forget about Jeffrey," he said, "Forget about all
the things that are bothering you. Don't do anything but
love me!"

Again he kissed her and the little Adam's clock on the
mantelpiece chimed the hour.

"I must go get dressed," he said, "Or we shall be late."

"I wish we didn't have to go," she said. "They are all
old friends and dear friends, but I don't want anyone but you,
my sweet, - my dear."

Boris and the witch doctor had taken a modest suite
of rooms on Jermyn Street. The rooms were above a grocery story
which prodly flaunted the statement that it was a grocery store
by the permission of his Gracious Majesty, the King, and displayed the royal arms, supported by a handsome Lion and Unicorn
in color and gilt.

Boris was seated in a chair, as dead as an Egyptian
carving. Loogo knelt in front of the fireplace. In this was a
grate and a glowing fire. From a black bag, reminiscent of
Africa, Loogo was taking the photograph of Mary Suffolk and the
letter which she had written to her brother. He had taken also
the skulls of three monkeys and other paraphenalia of magic.
Lastly, a powder which when thrown on the fire burned with a
strong blue flame. He had addressed himself to the monkey skulls
in African but to the photograph which he presently took in his
two hands he did not at first speak at all. It seemed as if he
were undergoing some strong convulsion of the spirit. You had
the feeling that he was trying to force his spirit into the
inanimate photograph. Or possibly, through the medium of the
photograph he was trying to force his spirit into the living

girl. At moments, it actually seemed as if the masses which went to make up the lovely shadowed image of the girl were actually moving and working. The eyes of the witch doctor blazed. Presently he laid himself flat down on the floor, clasping the photograph to his breast and became motionless. It could be seen that in the blazing eyes the light was beginning to die. The light dies altogether. He might have been another dead man.

Mary Suffolk had finished dressing for the dinner-dance and was being admired by her mother.

"My darling," said Mrs. Suffolk, "You look perfectly lovely, but ..."

"What is the matter?" asked Mary.

"There is a runner in your left stocking," said her mother crisply.

"But I hate to keep Arthur waiting, but I shall just have to run and change them. That's the second pair this week."

Mary ran into her dressing room, selected a fresh pair of stockings and sat down to put them on. She pulled up her pretty frock as much as was necessary and had almost completed the change when she noticed that the great black family cat, Niger, suddenly arched his back as if in fear and defiance, and spat. At the same moment, Mary had a feeling that she was not alone in the room and she hastily pulled down her dress. She arose to her feet and looked behind her. There was no one. She had a sensation of nausea. And then she seemed to hear a voice. Where this voice came from she did not know but the feeling that someone was speaking to her was so strong and she was so startled

146

-39--39-

that she spoke back.

"You'll come to me?" she said, "You will come to me?
Who are you?"

A door between the dressing room and the bedroom
where Mary's mother waited was ajar. Hearing her daughter
apparently carrying on a conversation with someone, Mrs. Suffolk
came into the dressing room and seeing no one to whom Mary's
words could have been addressed, very naturally said:

"Whom are you talking to?"

Miss Suffolk's nerves were badly shaken but she managed
to keep her self-possession.

"I actually thought," said she, "that somebody really
spoke to me. It was so real that before I knew it, I had answered. Mother dear, look at Niger!"

Niger had once more arched his back, but his fear and
animosity seemed now to be directed at Mary herself.

"Oh, mother dear," said Mary, "everything has been so
queer today, ever since Jeffrey's letter."

"Forget about Jeffrey's letter, my precious," said her
mother, "and run along to your young man and have a beautiful time."

"I feel so queer," said Mary. "Every now and then I
have had the feeling that I was not really myself and that I
was trying to be someone else. It is a horrible feeling."

The witch doctor had risen from the floor and had
finished laying out full evening-dress for his dead master. He
now laid himself down comfortably on the lounge and with hardly
any effort at all succeeded in animating the dead man and becoming himself, to all intents and purposes, lifeless. The dead

147

-40-

man's eyes began to blaze. He rose to his feet and began to undress.

In spite of her wish to be alone, with Dr. Martin, Mary had almost enjoyed the dinner and now when she was dancing and in her lover's arms, she felt almost secure. But during the dinner, it had happened that twice she had caught herself with that horrible feeling of trying to be someone else and now just as the dance finished and the young lady at the piano pretended to be in an exhausted state, the feeling came over her again. And a part of the feeling was an urge which drew her eyes to the stately row of french windows which formed one whole side of the room.

Daniel Quickley, an old friend and admirer of Mary's, happened to notice a curious expression of alarm and bewilderment that had come over her face and remarked to his late dancing partner.

"I wonder what's the matter with Mary. She looks happy enough when she is dancing with that long-legged lover of hers, but the moment she stops, she goes white and looks as if she was seeing things."

"Nothing but nerves, dear boy," said his partner, "If you were a pure young girl, rather religious and decidedly spiritual, and you knew that day after tomorrow night you would be alone in some hotel bedroom at the mercy of an amorous man, you would be nervous."

The mist drifted lightly past the French windows and out of this mist loomed Boris Odelosi. For a moment his blazing eyes held hers. The mist thickened and he vanished. She gasped

and with a violent effort at self-control, forced a smile to
her lips, leaned toward the girl on the piano seat and said:

"Darling, please don't stop. I want to dance."

"Darling," said the girl on the piano seat, and she
lifted her hands and pretended that there was no longer any life
in her fingers, "I am done in."

A young man seated himself on the extreme end of the
piano-seat and said:

"If you won't play, you'll sing, and you'll jolly well
like it. Move over!"

The girl moved further along the seat. The young man
moved to the center of it and his strong able fingers began to
crash out the opening chords of "You'll take the high road and
I'll take the low road." And the girl began to sing in a loud,
sweet, clear, young English voice.

Dr. Martin noticed his sweetheart's pallor.

"You are white as a sheet," he said, "I'll go fetch you
a glass of champagne."

"Don't leave me," she said quickly.

But he had turned away and did not hear her.

Mary hesitated a moment and then, unobserved by the
others, who had clustered around the piano to see just how much
noise they could possibly make, walked quickly to one of the
French windows, opened it, stepped out on the terrace and closed
the window behind her.

At a little distance, in a lovely old garden of clipped
Yew, half hidden in mist, she saw Boris Odelosi. She walked
slowly toward him.

When Dr. Martin returned with the glass of champagne, he did not see her anywhere and he whispered to a pretty little girl with a pug nose:

"I say, Myrtle, what's become of Mary?"

"If you must know," said Myrtle, who was a born tease, "I think it highly probable that she has rushed off somewhere or other to powder her nose."

Mary had sunk down on the marble bench beside Boris, but at a little distance from him.

"I don't know why I came to you," she said in her clear beautiful English voice. "I don't know why I sit here and let you talk to me about the dead."

"Because," said the dead man, but in the unmistakable voice of the witch doctor, "The dead will come back."

His eyes blazed into hers and drew closer to them.

"You came to me," he said, "because you could not help yourself. You are going to assist me in returning the dead to those who had loved them."

The girl had stiffened her shoulders but these now relaxed. It looked for a moment as if she were going to collapse. Boris Odelosi rose and walked off into the fog. When he was at a little distance, he stopped and looked back. Mary Suffolk rxm rose and followed him. The fog thickened about them and they vanished.

Since Mary Suffolk's mysterious disappearance, four days and nights had passed. Her mother was half mad with insomnia and anxiety. The narcotics which Dr. Martin had prescribed had had no effect.

"But, my darling," said her husband, taking her in his arms, "We are doing everything that is possible. I, myself, have thought of something which may just possibly help us to find a clue. After I have dropped our good doctor at the hospital, I am going straight to Scotland Yard to talk with Inspector Priestly. Now you keep a stiff upper-lip."

"And you are to lie down," said Dr. Martin," And you are to take two of the tablets. They are bound to work, they must."

Dr. Martin, himself, looked horribly the worse for wear. It was very difficult for him to hold staunchly to his professional manner. Mrs. Suffolk tried to be brave and contained. She accompanied them to the door of the living room, and said:

"Good luck to you both. You are dear, dear boys..."

In a suburb of London in the midst of old dilapidated grounds and lawns which had not been trimmed, stood a gloomy three-story house in the Georgian manner. The house had not been occupied for many years. In the cellars, under it, dating to a previous century, much of the house's furnishings had been stored. There was a confusion of chairs, tables, packing-cases, etc. Near the foot of a flight of stone stairs, worn hollow by generations of feet, knelt Loogo, the witch doctor. Opposite him knelt Mary Suffolk. At one side of her stood Boris Odelosi, holding a tall alter candle. Between Mary Suffolk and the witch doctor lay the body of a dead man. His hair was gray. He looked to have been the head of a middle class family.

The scene recalled that earlier one in Africa when Boris himself had been brought back to a semblance of life. Only

-44-

on this occasion, Boris was the torch bearer and the part of
the dancing girl was being acted by Mary Suffolk. The witch
doctor exerted his will and urged the dead man to come back.
He opened the dead man's shirt and when this was opened Mary
Suffolk at the witch doctor's command laid her left hand over
the dead man's heart. She laid her right hand over her own
heart and then leaned closer to the dead man, and closer until
the backs of her hands touched.

At a signal from the witch doctor, Boris shifted the
altar candle so that his dead body shut off the light from the
face of the other dead man.

The witch doctor seemed to redouble in energy and power.
He kept clinching and unclinching his hands in the well-remembered gesture of urgency as if with everything that he had that
was either physical or mental he was trying to force someone
else to do something which he resisted doing.

In the darkness something seemed to be happening.
Once more, Boris shifted the candle and it could be seen that the
dead man had struggled into a sitting position. The witch doctor
helped him to his feet and supported him until he had achieved
a sense of balance and could stand alone. The witch doctor turned
to Mary Suffolk.

She looked to be only half-conscious. He spoke to her
softly and gently:

"Again," he said, "you have helped to bring one back.
It is easier for you now. You are learning very fast. See!
Now he can stand alone. He has no brain. His heart does not beat.
Yet, he stands on his feet. He can walk and he will find his

way straight to his old home and to those who think they still
love him."

While he spoke, Mary Suffolk seemed to be coming out of
her trance, to understand what was being said to her.

Without thinking, perhaps, the witch doctor had for a
moment loosened his control over Mary Suffolk's hand. A partial,
perhaps a complete realization of the horrible thing which she
had just helped to bring back, gave one piercing scream, ran
swiftly to the flight of stone steps and up them.

The witch doctor watched her curiously but made no
attempt to check her flight or to pursue. He turned to the man
who had just been brought back.

The dead man walked a little fumblingly toward the
flight of steps and went up them. The witch doctor looked intently at the flame of the candle which Boris was carrying and
the flame went out. At first, nothing could be seen in the darkness but the two blazing eyes of the witch doctor. They resembled
the eyes of a great cat. But presently the white face of Boris
could be seen faintly and glimmeringly. He was following the
witch doctor toward the stair.

Mary Suffolk's father and Inspector Priestly, of Scotland Yard, had been talking for half an hour in the latter's
office.

"Please don't misunderstand me," said Mr. Suffolk, in
his gentle voice, "I don't mean that I actually believe in ghosts
and that sort of thing but to a certain extent I am what is
called 'psychic'. Several times I have had a presentiment that
a certain thing was going to happen and it has happened. In these

ways, my daughter is very much like me. So, you see, she felt
this presence in the room and felt it so strongly that when the
voice spoke to her she answered. Is it possible that somebody
at a distance succeeded in influencing my daughter?"

"Sometimes," said Inspector Priestly, "I think that
anything is possible."

"The Occult," continued Mr. Suffolk, "must sound like
the sheerest nonsense to most of the clever, practical men connected with Scotland Yard, and I am very grateful for the sympathetic way in which you have listened to me, and I do think that
it may be easier for you to find my daughter now that you have
more precise knowledge of her character."

"It may," said the inspector. "Let us hope so."

Through the fog and mists, Mary Suffolk, half ran, half
walked, without any objective. Almost she gave the impression of
a wounded bird fluttering, and indeed, she had been wounded and
most grievously. The realization had come to her proud sensitive
religious soul that she had been compelled to take part in
horrible and unforgivable rites. She believed in Heaven and
Hell. She believed herself to be one of the damned. The mist
cleared and she found herself in front of a small Gothic Church.
She went in. The place was lighted only by groups of candles
which burned in front of Saints. From the rose window above
the Gothic arch by which she had entered, colored light whose
source must have been a powerful arc lamp in the street without,
entered the place and picked up various details of architecture.
She turned and looked upward at this window. In the midst of it,
a medieval Christ had been nailed upon a cross. Knights in armor
and quaint ladies in fourteenth century costumes crowded about

the feet of the cross. The two thieves and various Christian symbols filled the sides and above was a great long narrow eye. Perhaps it was intended to be that of God, the Father. Mary Suffolk, without knowing what she was doing, spread out her arms as if she, too, were being crucified.

"Merciful Father," she cried, "What have I done? What Have I done? Is there no forgiveness?"

In the parlor of a small tasteless middle class house, the Reverend Father Richard Bentley together with his sweet-faced sister, a nun of the Urseline Order, were trying to console their mother. She was all in black. Her face was red and swollen with weeping. She wore an old-fashioned bonnet with long heavy streamers of crepe. That day she had buried her husband and she could not reconcile herself to the fact that her beloved was no longer in the house and would never again be in the house.

"That may well be," said the mother, "But I have given to His service my two children and now He has taken all that I have left me. We have laid your dear father in his grave. I shall never see him again. It isn't fair! I loved him and I want him. Wherever I look there is something to remind me of him and to wring my heart."

The nun with the sweet face said, "Come, mother darling."

The mother turned up her face so the son could kiss her and started obediently for the door but turned and began as if seemed to weep all over again.

"How," she said, "can I bear to look at that chair!" and she pointed to a very usual and rather comfortable-looking arm chair by the side of the table on which there was a lamp, "he always sat in that chair and now it will always be empty.

See, there on the table beside it is his pipe. I shall never again see him sitting in that chair and reaching for his pipe."

She began to sob and her daughter lead her from the room. The priest remained alone in the room, sad and thoughtful.

Presently the door into the hall opened quietly and the priest's father, the man whom he had that very day helped to bury, walked into the room and sat down. His eyes were dead eyes and there was no expression on his face. He looked as if he were made of wax. The priest perhaps trembled for a moment. It is sure that he crossed himself, but the voice in which he spoke to the dead man was clear and natural.

"Your spirit has been sent back to us, father," he said, "Have you come to guide us, to watch over us? Is there, perhaps, something that we are to do for you?"

The dead man, of course, did not answer. The priest approached closer to the body of his father.

"Can I help you to speak to me?" he said, and then as he drew still closer to the corpse his hand must have touched it because he said suddenly, "I thought you were a spirit but you are not."

He felt for signs of life but found none. The heart had no pulse, the breast did not rise and fall. The eyes were dead. It had not been difficult for the aesthetic to believe that the spirit of his father had entered the house but that which sat in the chair was no spirit. It was a corpse. Above the brows of the corpse he made the sign of the cross and then, turning his face upward, "I ask" he said, "for guidance - for understanding. Merciful Father, teach me what I should do!"

156

There was a kind of gasping sound. The priest turned
and saw that his sister had returned. He stepped quickly
to her and said, "Don't be frightened."

"But," said the nun, "It's father's spirit."

"No, my dear," he said, "It's not our father's spirit.
It is only his body. The heart does not beat; the breath come
and go."

Taking hold of his sister's arm they moved into the
hall. He closed the door between themselves and the dead man.

There the priest continued, "We loved him - we wanted
him. He came back and now...there is no place for him."

The priest's voice, hitherto in fine control, broke
nervously and became higher and shriller, "Now," he repeated,
"We don't want him."

"Ssh", said the nun, "Mother will hear you. Mother
mustn't know."

157

-50--50-

A policeman saw a woman struggling and swaying in the mist. He saw her sway into an entry, and clutch at the wall for support and sink in a heap to the pavement. He hurried to her side, flashing a torch. He saw that her hands were bleeding. He saw that the palms had been pierced as if some blunt instrument had been driven through them. Instinctively he looked down at her feet. The insteps of these had been pierced in a like manner.

He blew and blew his whistle. Presently in every direction footsteps could be heard ringing on pavements. A little crowd gathered.

"My Gawd," said one voice. "It looks like she had been nailed to something!"

A cockney voice cried, "I tell you she has been crucified!"

Mary Suffolk lay upon a bed in a private room of the hospital. Bandages had been drawn about her torn hands and feet. Her suffering had stilled her so she was undisturbed by the tense talk around her.

A group of alert, shrewd and forceful men, the foremost doctors of London, surrounded her bed. Dominating them was a little man with a body so tense and electric it seemed twisted. His bright eyes behind thick lenses had a strange brilliancy as though they had looked upon forces unfamiliar to the average eye. He was Professor Von Hecklemetz, the moremost philosopher and student of Occult lore in Europe. His age had gone on almost into the ageless, so superior in wisdom and experience was he to even the oldest of these veteran doctors and scientists. His black Inverness cape was thrown across his lap. His white hair stood

well out from his head. And his talk was in the quick precise
tones of challenge and debate:

"...your Science! ....Gentlemen, there are things
greater than your books....things beyong your Science. There
are forces....enormous forces that we do not understand----"

Here they interrupted him protesting, "But, Professor
Von Hecklemetz, you don't mean...not in this day...that a supernatural power caused these wounds! That is childish----"

At the word, "childish", the strange little professor
was on his feet challenging them, "Childish...Gentlemen, I
think we are going to find that this wound was not made by an
iron spike. I think that this wound and the one through her
right hand and those through her feet were not drilled by any
material agencies. I think they have been drilled by some
awful and contrite thought."

"By a what?" snapped one of the younger doctors.

"A thought," said Professor Von Hecklemetz, tapping
his forehead.

And then using tone and gesture to make his statement
even more impressive, he added, "Gentlemen, what you are seeing
here is one of the strangest manifestations of the human body
and the human soul....it is the STIGMATA!"

A murmur of protest came fromall parts of the group.

"Is there one among you who has ever seen the STIGMATA"?
the Professor asked. The men in the group shook their heads.

"But I have," said the little professor. "There have
been several cases, reported in various parts of the world again
and again. Honorable and intelligent men have examined them, and

and have testified to the facts. And the Church, approaching these cases with the utmost caution, with the most complete research, have accepted them as truths that can not be denied.

"Such wounds have come to sensitive persons like this beautiful girl lying here. Some great emotional shock has come upon her. Some demoniac force may have attacked her. And in her struggle for spiritual purity, to clense herself from some foul impulse that may have assailed her, she has cried out with all her despairing strength....and Gentlemen, these wounds have opened, wounds that are immortal in their significance."

Here the professor turned to the girl, directing one of the other doctors to bare the girl's right hand.

As the bandage is released, the blood wells up into the palm; and the professor asks an elderly and very famous doctor, "How long do you think it will take for these wounds to heal?"

"From ten days to three weeks."

"Good!" said the professor, "now we shall have our test. Your Science says from ten days to three weeks. I say these wounds will heal within three days of the time they first appear. So I have observed in such cases; and that time, Gentlemen, is now nearly past."

The startled looks in the faces of the doctors turned the professor's attention to the girl, and all stood tensely witnessing an amazing change. The fresh blood had ceased its flow!

"Look!", the professor commanded.

The astonished savants bent over Mary Suffolk to watch the strange activity. All blood had disappeared from the wound.

Slowly the torn flesh seemed to draw together. The dreadful
hole in the tender palm seemed to fill with firm tissue.

The professor turned to the awed group, "You see,
Gentlemen,.....a force beyond your Science."

Before the disconcerted men of learning could begin to
argue and compare, their comments, they were stopped by a sharp
change that had struck into this girl who had just now been so
lovely and so quiet. Dr. Martin moved impulsively to her side.

Mary Suffolk struggled as though contending with some
terrific force that was thrusting itself upon her. Her deep
gasps and wrenching movements told the doctors of the extreme
effort she was making to defend herself against the power that
was attacking her.

Then a great trembling shook her body, the desperate
commotion of being overcome. Her forehead lowered into wrinkles.
Her eyes took on a sharp and cunning and penetrating hardness.
Her mouth writhed with an evil vigor.

She began to speak, at first in low mutterings as though
still resisting, and then with sharp incisive tones.

While the others stared, unable to comprehend what was
happening, the little professor moved hastily nearer to her head,
bending over so he would miss no word. He was excited with the
terrible importance of what might be spoken.

Then from the face that had been so round and girlish
came the ominous voice of the Jungle, the voice of the witch doctor,
saying:"THE GRAVE WILL GIVE UP ITS OWN, UNTIL THE WORLD WILL BE
FILLED WITH THE WALKING DEAD."

Horrified by this voice from the girl he loved, Dr.Martin

cried out, "That's not her voice....it's someone else....
it's not Mary!"

"Of course not," said the professor, sympathizing
with Dr. Martin's anguish. "She is possessed with some unholy
Occult power."

Then he turned to the others, his voice vibrant with
excitement as he said, "Gentlemen....you heard that!....there
is our secret...there is our connection with these living
dead."

The girl, spent by her exertion, had dropped back
against the pillows. Leaving Mary to the care of Dr. Martin,
Professor Von Hecklemetz summoned the others from the room
with a soft but significant tone, "Come....Gentlemen...come..."

Soon all London was throbbing with terror at the
presence of these living dead. The newspapers cried out more
news of the shocking tragedy in each new edition. The horror
of these lifeless beings who were walking among the living had
aroused the city and the nation.

A council of the gravest importance had been called.
High state officials, the heads of the Police Department, the
foremost scientists and doctors were present.

A committee of doctors has just finished examining two
specimens of the walking dead. One is a woman, the other a man.

Professor Von Hecklemetz sits to one side, in the center
of a small group of national leaders. The doctors have been
whispering together in final consultation, their faces and
manners revealing their complete bafflement.

The alert little professor who has fought their scepticism

so long, now calls to the doctors, "You gentlemen of the Medical Science...if you are ready now----"

The doctors come to the professor and the officials and again the professor inquires, "Gentlemen...have you come to anything ----?"

Bewildered, they admit they have reached no explanation, for these two beings are dead...no evidence of animation...no response to tests for life.

The little professor stands and with characteristic gestures, speaks to them, "Gentlemen, you will admit there is nothing known to Medical Science that can release Rigor Mortis.. nothing that can stop decomposition. Yet you have these beings before you. Gentlemen, only when you believe in the Occult can this be explained...nothing but the Occult could accomplish this. Unless we find the seat of this evil influence---as this poor girl who is a defenseless agent has told us---this City of London is going to be over-run with the dead. And the living - they will go insane; they will kill themselves. And at night, the families who have buried their loved ones that day will sit around in mortal terror lest their dead stalk back into their midst. Gentlemen, unless this unholy Occult force is stopped, CIVILIZATION IS DOOMED!"

When Mary Suffolk had sufficiently recovered from
the shock to which she had been subjected she was taken home.
Here, her physical condition improved slowly but she was in a
mental state which drove Doctor Martin, because he could find
no way to remedy it, almost too desperation and which furnished
Von Hecklemetz a magnificent field for inquiry into the Occult.
Both men were frequent visitors.

Late one afternoon, Mary was resting in a deep chair.
Her lover had drawn his chair close to hers and held one of
her hands frankly in both of his. Von Hecklemetz flitted and
darted about the room. He seemed possessed with an untiring
energy and spirit of inquiry. He would plant himself directly
in front of Mary, ask her one or more leading questions and
would then dart away almost like a bird that had stolen something, while he appeared to digest her answers.

"Do you now have the feeling," he asked, "that
this evil spirit can take possession of you whenever it wishes?"

"Yes", she said, simply. "I no longer try to resist."

"Do you feel the presence before it possesses you?"

"Yes."

"Can you fight it?"

"No."

"When your own spirit comes back to you, you always
find yourself kneeling in front of this black man?"

"Yes." she said.

"At this moment do you feel that you are your own
normal self?"

"I shall never again," she answered, "be my normal self.

How can I be? The horror of what is happening to me is
too great."

While Von Hecklemetz darted off to digest these answers,
Doctor Martin leaned down and touched Mary's hand with his lips.
For many days he had realized that no words could be any comfort
to her. She was doomed, she thought - and damned.

"I have loved you so much," she said, "and we were
going to be so happy. Now this has happendd. I have to take
back the promise that I gave you."

Tears ran down her cheeks. Doctor Martin caught her
close to him and held her strongly.

"You can't take your promise back," he said, "I won't
let you. Somehow we are going to find a way to help you, to
save you."

Von Hecklemetz renewed the attack.

"Does this spirit," he asked, "possess you now more than
it did at first?"

"Soon," she said, "it will possess me all the time.

"When you have assisted him in bringing back the dead,
he asked, "do you feel an exceedingly wicked happiness?"

"Yes," she said.

"You and this black man, and soon others whom he will
initiate, will form a conspiracy to supplant the living with
the dead."

"When I am with him," she said, "nothing else, seems to
us worth thinking about." Her voice, calm enough but with the
deep note of anxiety,broke on the word. She drew her hands
from Martin's and got to her feet.

"Don't you see that I am damned," she said, "and
when the spirit possesses me altogether I shan't be fit to
live." She turned to her lover. "If you love me," she continued,
"you will give me something that will kill me. When I am no
longer myself ever at all will you promise to do that?"

He looked into her face with sad eyes and shook his
head.

Frantically, she insisted," Promise that when the
worst happens you will kill me!"

Von Hecklemetz came darting back from the further end
of the room.

"That would do no good," he said."He would send you
back to us. You would come back to this house yourself one of
the living dead. Those who had loved you would not have any
place for you. Your mother, perhaps, would die of horror."

Her voice broke pitiously, "Isn't there anything that
you can do?" she asked. Von Hecklemetz did not immediately
answer this question.

"When you were in the church," he said, "When you stood
there with outstretched arms you had suddenly the feeling that
you were being nailed to the cross. You felt as if spikes were
being roughly driven through your hands and feet. The pain
was frightful but you thought that you were being allowed to
atone for what you had done and this thought made you infinitely
glad?"

"Yes," she said.

The little man's eyes twinkled as if a sudden and

important thought had come to him.

"Tell me," he said, "did you feel that this frightful pain was washing your sins away?"

"Yes," she said.

He walked the length of the room. He seemed to be delighted with himself.

"Mary," said Dr. Martin, "Can't you possibly give us some clew as to where the black man keeps himself?"

Von Hecklemetz returned and shook his finger emphatically at Martin, "Suppose she could, what would you do?"

"I'd kill the beast with my bare hands," said the Doctor.

"At that moment," said Von Hecklemetz, "his evil spirit might have possession of Mary's body. You kill him and it will remain with her forever and that is the exact opposite of what must happen."

Once more the girl asked pitiously, "Is there nothing that you can do? Is there no way?"

"Yes," said Von Hecklemetz, "There is a way."

Hope came into her eyes, "Don't tell me what it is," she said, "because when his spirit controls me next time I might be forced to tell him."

"Do you trust me absolutely?" said the scientist.

"Absolutely," she said.

"And you, Doctor?" questioned Von Hecklemetz.

"Everything that you have told me," said Doctor Martin, has turned out to be true. At first, your talk about the power of the Occult seemed incredible, but the STIGMATA has proved

to me that Science leaves off where the Occult begins. You
ask if I trust you absolutely. I trust no man more. But
when you said just now that there is one way to save Mary,
something in the tone of your voice made me shudder. What are
we going to do?"

"I will tell you later and privately," said Von Hecklemetz, "and you will have to give your consent and you will
have to give your help, because it is the only way.

"Promise that you will," said the girl. Doctor Martin
did not immediately give the promise.

"My dear," said Von Hecklemetz, clicking his heels
together and bowing over Mary's hand which he kissed, "I have
some preparations to make. Good night!"

When the lovers were alone, Mary once more urged her
lover to give his word that he would not oppose Von Hecklemetz'
proposal whatever it was.

"Please promise," she said, "to help him.

"Suppose his way means terrible danger to you."

"What danger," she said, "could be greater than that
in which I am now standing? If you love me," she continued,
"you will help him."

She came then into his arms like a homing pigeon and he
held her close to his breast for a long time.

Night had fallen. Fog, thick and thin, filled the
London streets, drifted into rooms through open windows, drifted
into areaways and made a mystery of every light. Across the
street from the Suffolk's house, was a deep areaway from which

Doctor Martin and Von Hecklemetz kept an eye on the doorway of the Suffolk house while Von Hecklemetz unfolded his plan to save Mary and the reasoning upon which it was based.

"When Mary goes to the black man," he said, "his spirit will have possession of her body. He, himself, is lying down somewhere, a thing apparently without any life in it."

"What do we do?" asked Dr. Martin.

"We shall follow her," said Von Hecklemetz, "and wait. We shall wait until his spirit has left her and gone back to him. Then, we shall open fire upon his foul body. When he is dead his evil spirit will be out of his control. But if, by chance, his spirit does not leave her body, then we shall have to drive it from her body and back into his."

"How," asked Dr. Martin, "do we drive his spirit from her?"

Von Hecklemetz brandished an object tied in cloth which looked as if it might contain some tools. "With these!" he said.

"What is in that package?" asked the doctor.

"Do you remember what happened to Mary in the church? Her hands and feet were transfixed by imaginary spikes driven by an imaginary hammer."

"Of course," said Doctor Martin.

"The STIGMATA," continued Von Hecklemetz, "was a power against this evil force. While the wounds remain in her hands and feet, it could not possess her but when they healed and all traces of them were lost, his unholy spirit succeeded in forcing its way into a complete possession of her. Now she has no

longer the power to bring back upon herself these four
piteous wounds. We must do that for her. I have here four
real spikes and a hammer."

"Good God, man!" cried Doctor Martin, "are you stark,
staring mad?"

"She won't suffer any more than she suffered in the
church. I am not strong enough to manage the thing alone.
If you won't help me she is lost. She will become a creature
in which there is no wish and no thought that is not wicked.
There is but one way in which the woman you love can be saved
and restored to you. It is the only way." And then, with a
finger to his lips, he said, "Ssh! Look!"

The door of the Suffolk house opened and Maud Suffolk
came out. Even across the street in the misty twilight it
could be seen that the eyes were not hers. They were cruel,
wicked eyes.

The street in which the Suffolks lived was suburban.
It was shaded by two rows of fine old Elms. At the nearest
corner was a cab-stand which at the moment afforded parking
space for two taxicabs on the watch for fares. Toward these
vultures of the night Maud Suffolk moved swiftly with purposeful
steps. Martin and Von Hecklemetz, making use of the tree trunks
to shield themselves from discovery, followed her at what they
conceived to be a safe distance.

Miss Suffolk commandeered the first cab she came to
and drove off at a sharp pace. The gentlemen followed her in
the remaining. taxi.

She lead them a wild chase through one suburb after

another. At times, because of places the fog was so heavy,
they feared that they would lose her.

These fears were groundless. The vehicle containing
Mary Suffolk came to a stop on the edge of a little wood. She
alighted, paid her fare and disappeared among the trees. Doctor
Martin and Von Hecklemetz followed her on foot as soon as it
seemed safe for them to do so. They followed her to a three-
story Georgian house standing in the midst of unkept grounds.
They saw her go up three broad, shallow steps and enter the
house by the front door. Presently and very cautiously they
followed.

The floors of the house were thick with dust and it
was easy to pick out the direction in which she had gone.

The marks of feet, going and coming many times, had
made a distinct pathway diagonally from the front door to a
smaller door at the right side of the hall under the stairhead.
Otherwise, the dust had not been disturbed for years. The path
through the dust lead them into the subterranes of the house
and indeed to the head of a certain stone stair, the treads of
which had been worn hollow by generations of feet. As they
descended a few steps, a scene hitherto cut off by an arch which
might have been Roman, was gradually disclosed. At one side
of a narrow arched cellar there sat in a high-backed oak chair
a man who was obviously dead. He answered to Miss Suffolk's
description of the man with whom she had gone away from the
dinner dance. In his hand, which rested on the arms of the
chair, he held a tall altar candle. Within the circle of light,
lying upon his back, his hands folded upon his breast, in the

dress of a gentleman's servant, lay a negro with snow white
hair. His eyes were dead and staring; he neither drew a breath
nor moved a muscle. Across from the dead man who sat in the
chair, was an immense arched door of heavy oak planks, bound
together by ornamental irons.

Crouching on the stairway, looking over the solid stone
balistrade, Doctor Martin and Von Hecklemetz saw Mary Suffolk
walk slowly forward and kneel beside the body of the prostrate
negro. So kneeling, she began to sway her body and make those
clinching and unclinching urgent gestures with her hands with
which the reader is already familiar.

Doctor Martin, driven by hatred and without regard to
reason, leveled the automatic which he carried naked in his
hand, rested the long ominous barrel on the top of the balistrade and began to take a careful, coldly calculated aim at the
negro.

"Wait - wait!" whispered Von Hecklemetz, "Wait till the
soul is entirely out of her body and has gone back into his."

In withdrawing his weapon, a stone no longer bound to
its place by mortar was dislodged and fell with a startling
thud to the floor of the cellar. Mary Suffolk lept to her feet
and turned toward the sound. Her eyes, when she recognized
her lover and the professor blazed like a tiger's. The two
men hurried down the stair toward her.

"Don't use that gun," whispered Von Hecklemetz, "His
black soul is still in her body."

While they were advancing toward her, a change had come

over Mary Suffolk. The spirit of the witch doctor which was
in her and controlled her was not only an evil spirit but
a cunning, dexterous, quick-thinking spirit. Her eyes were
no longer so burning bright. The scowl of hatred had been
smoothed from her forehead. She turned to Von Hecklemetz, and
with the voice of the witch doctor, truly and fearful and a
wonderful thing to have heard, she spoke,

"For one who is so learned, it is incredible that you
should so have blundered."

Von Hecklemetz, with a twinkle in his eye, but a twinkle
full of malice, said, "Blundered! What makes you think so?"

With eyes becoming a little more defiant, she said,
"The one chance - the only chance you will ever have to
destroy me, you have thrown away."

"You forget," said Von Hecklemetz, "there is a power
far greater than that of evil, and with this power I will drive
your wicked soul into that vile body lying there, and then
destroy it."

This did not alarm her. It seemed more to antagonize
her, and with a sneer of contempt, she said,

"Of the Occult, you have learned very little."

"But enough to defeat you," cried Von Hecklemetz.

Unwrapping the package he carried with him, he held
aloft a hammer and four large iron spikes. At the sight of
these implements of torture, the spirit of the witch doctor
seemed to be burning its way through her eyes. It penetrated
the thick lenses of the eye-glasses worn by Professor Von Hecklemetz. It seemed to be penetrating through Von Hecklemetz' eyes

into his very soul. Slowly, the professor seemed to lean forward; slowly, he took half a step forward; his body swayed but he fought against this unholy force. With difficulty, he raised his hand. Fighting all the while against this evil power, his hand reached his glasses and he removed them from his eyes. A relief came over him. He relaxed as he stepped back and said,

"Without my glasses, your eyes grow very dim. They lose their effect."

But the soul of the witch doctor was not ready to accept defeat. Once again, her eyes lost the burning light. Once again, the scowl of hatred was slowly leaving her face. She turned to Doctor Martin and with a voice that was softer, but still that of the witch doctor, she said,

"Arthur, though his spirit is within me and I am compelled to use his voice, I, Mary Suffolk, know what I am saying. There is a way - a way to release me from his control."

Martin grabbed at this hope like a drowning man grabs at a straw.

"How - tell me how!" he said.

Mary Suffolk continued, "When his soul re-enters his body, - if you will allow him to leave here in peace, he will go back where he came from, I will be free forever."

"I will promise - promise with all my soul," cried Doctor Martin.

Her eyes seemed to twinkle with pleasure. She reached out her hand towards him, and said,

"Then give me the revolver."

"Never!" cried Von Hecklemetz, as he placed his
glasses to his eyes again, "Never! I, too, know some of your
thoughts - especially the one to get possession of that gun
and kill us both."

She seemed to ignore the professor. Slowly, she took
a step towards Doctor Martin, and still pleading with the
voice of the witch doctor, she said,

"Arthur, I have not the physical strength to fight you
and get the revolver. Can't you understand that it is I, only,
whom he will trust?"

Professor Von Hecklemetz' shrewd eyes were watching
every move she made; watching Martin as he stood before him
still hesitating to give in; watching as she took another step
towards him. The voice, with its pleading tone continued,

"Is it not better this way than to subject me to the
awful torture you have planned? I have gone through that
torture, Arthur, please don't make me suffer it again."

As she placed her arms gently about his neck, her eyes
began to blaze - blaze with a fire that penetrated into his.
His intentions were to crush her to him - to hold her safely
in his arms and never let her go, but these thoughts seemed
to leave him. He stood there staring into her eyes. Then,
slowly he removed one of her arms from around his neck and was
placing the gun in her hand, when, as quick as a rattlesnake
strikes, Von Hecklemetz struck - and the gun flew from her
hand across the floor. Seizing her by the arms he tried to
thrust her in the direction of the heavy oak door. Angered by

175

what looked like an unprovoked assault upon the woman he loved, Doctor Martin shouted,

"Have you gone mad?"

"No," shouted the little man, "You're the mad one," and still seeking to overpower her, he added, "A moment more and we both would have been dead."

These words had perhaps no significance for Doctor Martin. He saized Von Hecklemetz roughly by the arm and shook him loose from the girl.

"Leave her alone!" he said and glared angrily at him. The littleman glowered back. The girl stood motionless and her eyes blazed. They were wholly evil and at thesame time deeply thoughtful and astute. Speaking more gently, Doctor Martin said,

"But didn't you hear her say that the gun had to be in her possession?"

"You fool!" said Von Hecklemetz, "Did you think that it was Mary's soul that was talking? Mary didn't say it. It was said to us by that cunning, unholy spirit which possesses her and which seeks her destruction."

There came from Mary's throat a scream of rage like nothing earthly. It was the cry of an animal - a jungle cry. Her eyes on fire, she made a dash for the gun. But Von Hecklemetz was too quick for her. Again, he grappled with her and now, brought to his senses by that terrible cry, Doctor Martin came to his aid. They tried to pinion her arms but she fought them like a wild cat, biting and scratching. By the time that they had dragged her to the oak door and pressed her against it, both men were bleeding. Doctor Martin was a powerful man and had uncommon skill with his hands, but it was all he could do with the help of the professor to hold her with her back to the door, her right arm doubled so that she could not use it, and her left arm extending from her body at a right angle, the palm of the hand outward. She still screamed and struggled with the utmost fury of energy. Martin was handicapped by the fact that he could not look at the awful eyes which blazed in her head. She no longer seemed to resemble the woman he loved, even physically. But when the little man cried, "Spike her to the door!" he could not and it was Hecklemetz, wielding his hammer with a vim and accuracy which was surprising in so small and old a man, who nailed first her left hand to the door, and then her right. Now, he knelt to drive the spikes through her feet.

Meanwhile, a change had come over the prostrate negro as Miss Suffolk's screams and struggles became less. Light appeared in his dead eyes. They began to twinkle and snap. His wicked soul, driven from her body by the symbolism of the Crucifiction, was returning as swiftly as it could to his. Presently, his eyes blazed just as hers had blazed. He got to his knees and stealthily began to creep toward the automatic pistol which lay on the floor.

Suddenly, Von Hecklemetz became aware that Mary Suffolk's screaming and the struggling had stopped altogether. He looked upward. Mary Suffolk's head had fallen forward and sideways on her breast. Her face had at once a look of great suffering and peace. She seemed symbolic of a holy thing.

But to that quick thinker, Von Hecklemetz, the symbol
told a different story.

"Quick, man - quick!" he cried.

Halfway towards the gun and where he had been lying,
the witch doctor crouched and looked with horribly concentrated,
tigerish eyes into the faces of the two men. He was careful
not to cast a glance at the bleeding symbol which had driven
his unholy spirit from the body of the beautiful girl and back
into his own.

From his crouching position he sprang suddenly for the
heavy automatic. But Martin was the first to reach it. The
heavy bullet traveling at high velocity checked the spring of
the witch doctor and brought him, crumpled and writhing, to
the floor. In the automatic there remained eight cartridges.
One after the other with a perfect fury of speed and hatred,
Doctor Martin emptied these into the body of the screaming,
writhing negro. The last shot,delivered at close quarters,
drilled a hole half an inch in diameter into his right temple.
The witch doctor lay still in death.

A silence followed - a silence as quiet as the tomb.
Suddenly, a sound directed their attention to the dead man who
had been sitting in the high-backed chair. It was the sound of
the altar candle falling to the floor where it still burned
and sputtered. As they looked, the dead man collapsed in the
chair, toppled over and sprawled on the flagstone floor,
putting out the light of the candle. There was darkness in
which could be heard the cool, measured tones of Von Hecklemetz

"SO IT WILL BE WITH ALL THE OTHERS, DEATH HAS
RECLAIMED ITS OWN."

Mary Suffolk, her mind at peace, her loving troth
replighted, soon recovered from her wounds.

Whenever the little river boat came up from Wamba
with the mail, Trelawney made an effort through that medium
to keep up with the times. He attended to his correspondence
and read all the newspapers religiously. But Suffolk, a ghastly
shadow of himself, with haunted eyes, neither opened his letters
nor glanced at the news. Trelawney sometimes feared that his
youthful companion would end by goingmad. An item in the
London"Times", dated more than two months ago, caught his eye.
He read it through swiftly and a look of relief and happiness
came into his eyes.

"Cheerio old top," he cried, "Here's news for you."
They have got them both, "said Trelawney, "Both Boris and that
damned witch doctor and they have both been burned to ashes."

THE END

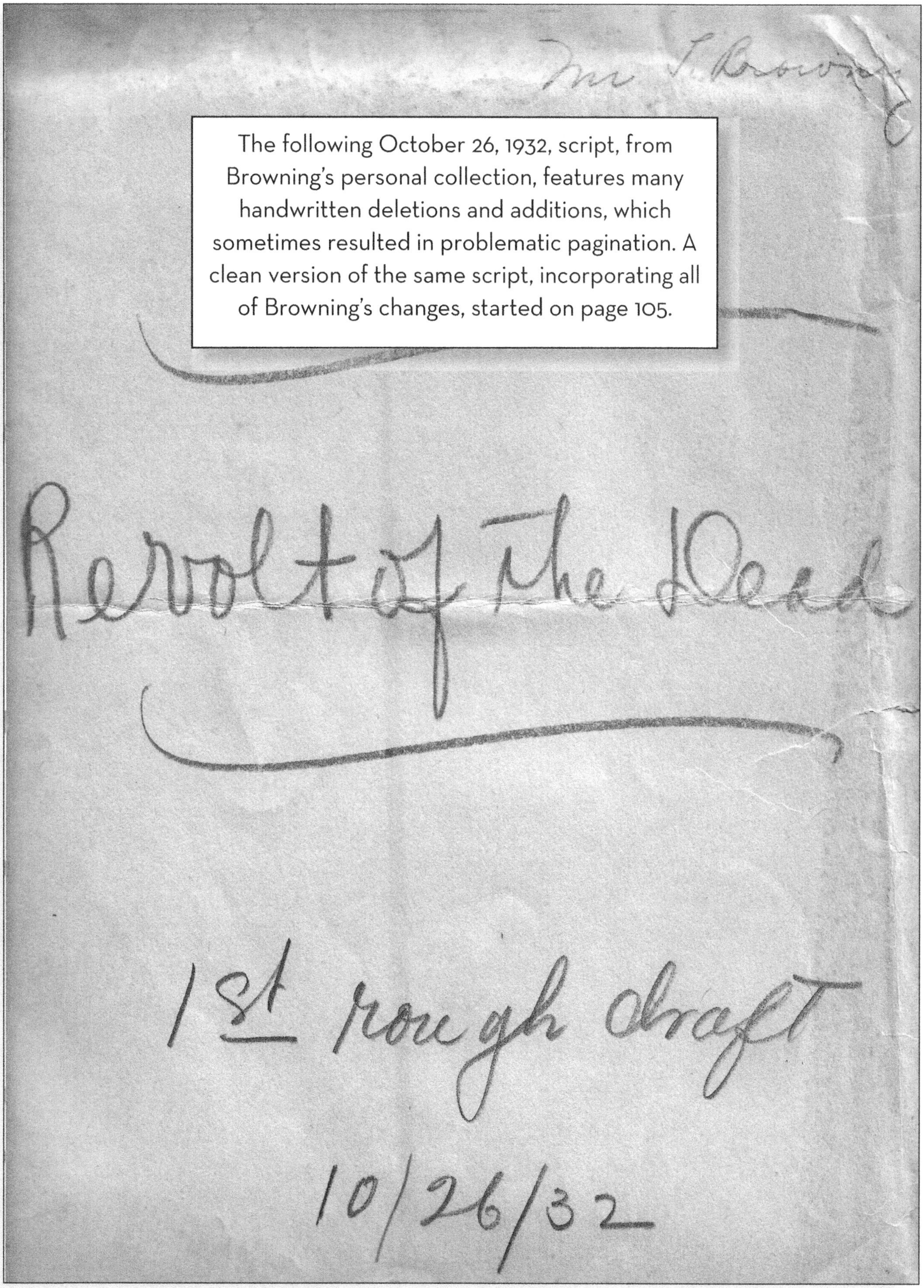

The following October 26, 1932, script, from Browning's personal collection, features many handwritten deletions and additions, which sometimes resulted in problematic pagination. A clean version of the same script, incorporating all of Browning's changes, started on page 105.

Revolt of The Dead

1st rough draft

10/26/32

180

THE REVOLT OF THE DEAD

3.

The negro, Bulbo, black as the ace of spades, his eyes shut, lay flat on his back and moved only as much as was necessary to stir the air in the living room of the bungalow. This movement was performed entirely by Bulbo's left foot between whose great toe and the next the cord which passed through the wall of the house and moved the punkah fan was firmly held. Bulbo was not asleep. Unusual sounds from the jungle or the river were instantly registered by various wrinklings of his low forehead and twitchings of his ears.

If the punkah moved the air in the living room it did not cool it and George Alfred Trelawney was wet through and the pencil with which he was footing a column of figures slipped in his hand. Trelawney was a long legged Englishman of forty-five but since his teens he had not often seen England. His life's work had been among savage peoples and savage climates. His hair was graying, his skin was tinged with the unmistakable yellow which tells of an unhappy liver. His lean handsomely carved face had a look of temper.

But his expression ought to have been happier because he was now convinced that with the help of young Suffolk and the Hungarian engineer, Boris Odescalchi, he had located and defined an oil dome of incalculable value.

The living room had a certain picturesqueness due to somewhat disordered use of native weapons and fabrics.

From somewhere far off in the jungle there came from time

to time a faint and muffled sound of drums. Sometimes Trelawney
could not be sure that he was hearing drums or the beating of his
own pulses. Since the preceding midnight the thermometer had
stood at 103 degrees in the shade. ¶Three bedrooms opened off the
living room. Through a fourth open door could be seen one corner
of a makeshift shower bath and through a fifth a rectangle of
savage landscape in the midst of which lay rather than flowed a
dark river. Into this rectangle stepped the Reverend Mr.Morrison,
the missionary. Mr. Morrison wore a jacket and trousers of white
linen and a pith helmet. The only thing about his dress to denote
his calling was a gold cross suspended from his neck by a narrow
black ribbon. A stronger note of black was forced by a band of
crepe stitched to his right sleeve. Mr. Morrison was perhaps
thirty-five years old. He had the Zealot's eye, the Zealot's look
of self-confidence and a certain mock humility so often associated
with the pulpit.

Trelawney detested missionaries in general and this one in
particular, but the knowledge that this one was in deep trouble
and sorrow brought him to his feet with a pleasant word of welcome
and an extended hand. Mr. Morrison touched the band of crepe on
his arm and said:

"We have decided not to feed any longer on hope. It is a
month today since our darling little daughter disappeared. That
she should have survived the dangers and pitfalls of the jungle is
unthinkable. He who has taken her back into His care alone knows
her fate. We console ourself with the belief that it was swift
and painless. Perhaps the quick silent spring of a leopard and
one killing blow of its paw."

"She was a dear little thing," said Trelawney, " I cannot

182

tell you how profoundly sorry I am for you and your wife.

Stifling a yawn, his hair tousled as if he had been lying down young Bradley Suffolk emerged from one of the bedrooms.

He shook hands with Mr. Morrison and said that he was glad to see him.

"And where," asked Mr. Morrison, "is the third musketeer? Where is Boris?"

"Where he usually is," said Suffolk, "back there in the village studying native manners and customs, witchcraft, voodoo, and what have you."

"The first thing we know," said Trelawney, Mr. Boris Odeschalchi will go completely native and show up with a ring in his nose and a black wife."

"Heaven forfend," sighed Mr. Morrison.

"And that," continued Trelawney, "will be a loss to the British Exploration Company limited of a very capable engineer. That young man has a nose for oil.

"Oil," said Suffolk, "is his business. I wish he would stop sticking his nose into so many other things that aren't."

"What I really came for," said Mr. Morrison, "is to thank you for all you have done for us, and all you have tried to do, in our sorrow and to say goodbye."

"You're not leaving us!" exclaimed Trelawney.

"For a month only," said Mr. Morrison, "My duty is here and my duty is clear, but Mrs. Morrison is terribly pulled down and I have the hope that a month of sea breezes will bring back the color to her cheeks. Will you kindly convey my respects to Mr. Odeschalchi when you see him? He and our little baby girl were great friends."

Mr. Morrison turned and really fled from a sudden show of

-4-

emotion with which he was threatened.

"Did you hear that! " exclaimed Suffolk indignantly, "convey his respects to Mr. Odeschalchi! He and the little girl were such great friends!"

"Well they were great friends, weren't they," said Trelawney, "he was always playing with her, giving her candy, chocolate."

"Yes," said Suffolk, "to get her confidence and trust. I would bet plenty of money that Mr. Boris Odeschalchi knows where she is at this minute."

"Just because you happen to hate a man," said Trelawney, "is no reason why you should talk nonsense about him."

"It isn't hatred," said Suffolk, "it's instinct. The man's a rotter. He wouldn't stop at anything to get his way. I believe that he knows where that child is and I believe he took her there."

"What you need," said Trelawney, "is a months vacation in cold climate. The next thing we know, you will be seeing things."

During all this while the long punkah fan had been swinging slowly to and fro. But now it faltered and stopped. Bulbo had fallen asleep.

Trelawney simply stepped out on the veranda and kicked him. Bulbo did not open his eyes but once more the foot which held the punkah cord began to move rhythmically.

II

The huts of the village had been built in two long rows. The central space between them served as a street. At their backs were scrubby plantations; corn, bananas, indian hemp and Papaias. Beyond these the tall dark jungle was like a threat. The houses were shaped like old fashioned beehives. The villagers usually a boisterous jolly lot were all in the street but there was no laughing and the only talk was in hushed tones. The villagers seemed to be laboring under a strong but suppressed excitement. It was not yet night but the village was already completely in shadow. One of the huts was much larger than the others. Out of this presently stepped Boris Odeschalchi, the Hungarian engineer. He was a tall man with strong forceful features and there was a something strange and unforgetable about him. His eyes at once shone with a fine intelligence and had in them a hint of madness. He was followed into the open by Loogo the witch doctor. Loogo wore none of the insignia of his calling. His face and body were not painted and his breech clout differed in no way from those worn by the other men of the tribe. His features were not negroid. They were thin and sharp. He had a commanding brow. His hair was snow white. He carried himself and moved with a certain majesty. Although his body was smooth and firm he looked to be a very old man.

A complete hush had come over the villagers. The engineer and the witch doctor with fitting strides walked the length of the village street in a purposeful way and disappeared into the jungle. The villagers exchanged looks which were at once knowing and awed.

Having entered the jungle the witch doctor took the lead. He was careful to step where his feet would leave no track and the engineer imitated him. They came to a stream and followed it for some distance by wading. They came to an outcrop of granitic rock. Here they left the stream and came at last by devious windings to a hut so cunningly and secretly hidden that it could not even have been seen from an airplane. The hut contained two comfortable good natured looking black women and a female child. The child wore a little crown of flowers and a little girdle of flowers. She was a beautiful child. Her hair was golden and her skin was white. She was not more than three or four years old.

-6-

She ran to Boris Odeschalchi holding out both her arms. He swung her lightly from the ground and gave her a smacking kiss.

"Are you happy Doris?" he asked. "Plenty to eat? Plenty of toys?"

"Yes," said the child, "But I want to go back to Daddy and mumsy. I want to go back tonight. Say I can go back tonight. Promise."

The witch doctor who had been regarding the pair in a detached way now spoke one word in clear, precise, impeccable english:

"Promise," he said.

"Alright," said Boris to the child, " I promise."

Boris put the child down and one of the women came forward and took her by the hand. Loogo murmured a word in native and the two women accompanied by the child went out of the hut, but the child looked back at Boris over her shoulder and smiled and he called gayly to her, " see you later."

Loogo's quick eyes caught sight of what had perhaps once been the white child's hair ribbon. He picked this up and dropped it into the remaining embers of the cook fire where it shriveled, blackened, twisted like a snake and became ashes. Then he straighten himself and appeared to listen. He smiled suddenly and said,

"They come."

There came into the hut two tall and magnificent negroes bearing torches. They took positions on opposite sides of the hut and stood motionless, two magnificent candle sticks of bronze. Two women followed them in from the night. The first was a very old woman, withered and shrunken. She carried in her hands a tray skilfully woven from Pandanus leaves. On this tray rested a long straight narrow knife of bright steel. The second woman was young

186

and by African standards, most beautiful. She wore flowers in
her hair and a girdle of flowers about her waist. She carried
in her hand a cage woven from bamboo splits. In this cage was a
white dove.

Loogo took the knife in his right hand, with his left hand he
opened the door of the cage and withdrew the dove. For a moment
the dove ~~the dove~~ fluttered and then lay still. He opened his hand
as if to show that this stillness was not caused by any pressure of
his fingers. It was as if the dove had died, then presently it
showed signs of life and began to struggle, to turn, and get on its
feet. But Loogo's hand closed upon its legs, its tail, and the
tips of its wings, imprisoning them. He held the dove so that his
breast was presented to the point of his knife. Very slowly he transfixed   the dove with the knife so that the point of this stood
out between the wing shoulders, then loosening his left hand he
lifted the dove, empaled on the point of the knife, high over his
head where it made desperate efforts to fly, beating frantically
with its wings.

Once more Loogo took the dove in his left hand. This time
he withdrew the knife from its breast. There was no blood upon
the knife and when Boris ran his fingers delicately through the
breast feathers of the dove he could not find any wound or any
drop of blood. Loogo returned the knife to the tray from which he
had taken it.

From the night surrounding the hut, came now a sudden soft,
throbbing insistent rhythm of drums. The girl who had brought the
dove to Loogo now advanced with steps which kept time to the drums
and held out her hands for the dove. In each hands she held one
of the bird's wings and one of its legs. The rhythm of the drums
increased in tempo and with it the movements of the girl's feet

-8-

and body. As she danced she looked upward at the dove. The
expression on her face was that of a Sadist, a torturer. Steadily
the speed of the drum rhythm increased and with them the speed of
the girl's dancing and it looked now to Boris as if she were trying
to tear the dove apart.

As the dove's breast tore apart and blood flowed, the girl's
dancing went into a kind of frenzy. The blood ran down her arms
and dropped on her upturned face. Suddenly the music of the drums
came to a full stop and so also the dancing of the girl. She bent
forward, lower and lower until the dove was above the knife. Blood
fell upon the knife. Almost it seemed as if the dove were a sponge
which the girl was wringing. When the knife had been sanctified
with the blood of the dove, the drums again began to beat, this
time with an incredible agitation and fury. The girl kept time
with her feet and body, her face now like that of a maniac, upturned
to the bleeding, mangled dove. The dance came to a sudden, and to
Boris, an unexpected end. The girl gave one long piercing scream
and fell to the floor in convulsions.

The drums had stopped beating. There was complete silence.
Everything was still except the shuddering, convulsed body of the
dancer. When Loogo brought the palms of his hands smartly together
they made a sound as sharp and startling as a pistol shot.

Two women came in out of the night, mastered the frantic
struggles of the dancer and carried her away. Loogo dismissed the
torch bearers with a curt gesture. He and Boris and the woman who
had brought the knife were alone in the hut. Loogo examined the
knife to see if it had been well blooded. In returning it to the
tray he said solemnly:

"In hoc signo vincimus."

"By jove! " said Boris, "Latin!"

188

-9-

The women turned and went out of the hut.

"Is there any language that you don't speak," asked Boris,

"Not any, " said Loogo.

"That is the most amazing thing about you. You have never been out of this fever jungle and yet you can speak all the polite languages under the sun."

" My astral body, " said Loogo, "has been a great traveller. It has been in Germany, France, England, America often. I have a quick ear."

"Will my astral body be able to go on journeys?" asked Boris.

"Of course," said Loogo, "and even now with my help you could travel to Budapest and see your Father and your Mother. Would you like that?"

"I am a little homesick for them, " said Boris simply.

"Then lie down on this mat," said Loogo.

Boris lay down on the mat and Loogo squatting beside him looked him fixedly in the eyes and made quick passes over his cheeks and temples.

"Your astral body, " said Loogo, "is restless. It suffers from vanderlust and heimweh. You are going home."

Boris's eyes closed, his entire body stiffened convulsively, and then relaxed. A dead man could not have seemed more still. The witch doctor smiled. It was the smile of an old man who is giving pleasure to a child.

Odeschalchi's parents, his younger brother Paul and his two sisters were at dinner. It was a warm night and the french windows along one side of the room were open.

Suddenly Madame Odeschalchi turned in her chair with extended arms and a happy look on her face. "Boris," she said, "my darling."

-10-

But there was no Boris standing beside her. Odeschalchi and his son were on their feet. The older man's forehead was beaded with sudden sweat. The eyes of the two sisters were wide with amazement.

"Where is Boris! " exclaimed the mother, "he was here. He called me motherkin. He laid his cheek against mine. Boris where are you hiding?"

Her expression had changed to one of perplexity and anxiety.

"Did none of you see him?" she asked.

"I didn't see him," said her husband, "but I felt that he was in the room.

"So did I, so did I," said the daughters.

"I know that he was in the room," said Paul.

The family rushed on to the balcony on which the french windows opened but there was no one there, only the night set thickly with lights.

Loogo continued to smile.

"You have traveled, " he said, "you have seen your father and your mother. ~~You have seen the stag's head over the dining room mantelpiece and now you are coming swiftly back to Africa.~~"

He made passes over the cheeks and temples of the Hungarian. A look of wonder came over Boris's face and his eyes opened.

"I saw them, " he said, "and I wanted to stay a long time. My Father looks very old, but I couldn't stay."

He got to his feet and shook himself. He was now completely out of the trance into which he had been thrown.

"Loogo," said Boris, "with the knowledge and power that your people have had for thousands of years, how is it possible for you to be driven back by the white man's civilization?"

-11-

"There are many reasons," said Loogo, "Cannon, warships, airplanes, whiskey and greed."

"But", said Boris, "your power , the power of the occult is so much more wonderful than science. You began where science leaves off. If you wish to know what is going on in London or New York, you have only to go and see for yourself and nobody can see you or hurt you. It is incredible that Science should have defeated the occult and driven it to the wall."

"But", said Loogo, "the battle is not finished. Science has not defeated the occult. Not yet. Come."

They went out into the night and retraced their steps to the village. By one of the outlying huts, Loogo haulted.

"I am going to show you something," he said, "that ~~you have not yet seen.~~ ~~Science can not do,~~
                                            the
. They approached windows of the hut which stood open and looked in. The interior was illumined by a small fire and by candle nuts set on iron spikes. Over the fire was suspended an iron pot and a comely negress was stirring its contents. Two bright eyed children watched this operation with interest.

On the edge of a cot bed, looking and not looking, dumb, sightless, without thought, sat a dead man. Garlands of withered flowers hung about his neck and loins. He made no motion of any kind.

"A Zombie," whispered Boris.

The upper lip of the witch doctor curled scornfully.

"A Zombie," he said, "is only a wretched man who has been drugged. That man is a dead man who has come back.

"Horrible," said Boris with a shudder.

"Not to us," said Loogo, "We are used to them. The woman

wanted her husband back so I gave him to her. But I cannot give him back his soul. But I can lend him my own soul. Would you like to see that?"

They went into the hut and after he had greeted the woman, Loogo laid himself down on the cot on the edge of which the dead man was sitting. It could be seen by the strained muscles of Loogo's face and the blazing concentration of his eyes that he was making some tremendous effort of the will. Boris watched the eyes of the witch doctor. For a time they seemed to be on fire. Slowly the fire in them began to die. Boris looked at the dead eyes of the dead man. Light was coming into them. They moved in their sockets. The dead man's brows twitched. The dead man opened his mouth and spoke in the voice of the witch doctor.

"You see," the voice said, "he talks english just as well as I do."

The dead man turned to the woman and still with Loogo's voice but now in the native tongue, spoke to her and seemed to be saying kind and appreciative things. He spoke also to the children, addressing them by their names and they ventured a step or two in his direction, but then as quickly as the light had come into the dead man's eyes, it went out of them and Loogo's eyes which had seemed for a time like those of a dead man, became once more bright with the fire of his intelligence. The witch doctor got up from the bed.

"If they loved each other," asked Boris, "why didn't he embrace her and kiss her when he had the chance?"

"It was not his soul that was in him, " said Loogo, "But mine, and my soul does not happen to wish for the embraces of this particular woman."

192

"And do your people," asked Boris, "really want to have their dead with them?"

"Yes," said the old man, "all those who love their departed want them. ~~We have a place for them."~~

"In civilization," said Boris, "there is no place for the dead. If the dead were to return to those who love them, it would drive them insane. to give them sitting around like this."

"It would do what?" asked Loogo quickly.

"Drive them insane," said Boris. "Drive them mad."

The old man looked like someone who has been suddenly struck with a tremendous thought. He looked younger. He held himself more erect.

"It would drive them mad," he said.

They went out into the night. The hut to which the dead man had returned was a little removed from the village. There was a piece of black forest between. The moon which had risen, made gleaming high-lights on the leaves and trunks of trees. Through the trees, moving listlessly and without purpose, came a little procession of five dead men who had come back. Boris and the witch doctor drew a little to one side while the dead men passed by.

"More of them," said Boris.

The old man seemed to be laboring under a great excitement. He pushed Boris ahead of him as if very eager now to get back to his own house and he exclaimed in a strong voice as they hurried on:

"There will be more of them, hundreds of them, thousands of them."

-14-

The village street was crowded with men, women and children in a suppressed state of excitement. The drums throbbed with strong insistence, many of the villagers had painted their faces and bodies with horrible designs. Many wore head dresses of nodding Ostrich feathers. Some had concealed their faces behind hideous masks. The warriors carried shields of rhinoceros and hippopotamus hide and clusters of throwing and stabbing spears. As Boris and Loogo began to pass through this crowd toward the house that was bigger than the other houses, the tempo and the strength of the drums increased and the crowd kept time with a rhythmic stamping of the feet. Eyes and teeth gleamed. Some of the younger people shuddered as if they were cold. Some of the older women rocked slowly on their feet and made a sound of low moaning. At the entrace to his house, Loogo paused for a moment and looked up at the moon dripping with light. Then he passed into the house, followed by Boris. Against the walls of the house, hung all the regalia and paraphernalia of a great witch doctor. Feather cloaks and capes of great beauty, hideous masks. Ranged along the walls like whitewashed stones in gardens, were skulls of enemies who had been killed in battle. Loogo took from the wall a cloak of black and white feathers. The white feathers made between the shoulders the design of a huge skull. But the rhythm of the drums and excitement in the street without, were too strong to be resisted, and Boris went back to the door and looked out. The excitement of the people like the tempo of the drums was in a steady crescendo. Boris was almost unnerved by the sheer savage- ness of it. When his eyes once more returned to the witch doctor, this one, by a swift and sure use of pigments had been transformed into a thing of majesty and horror toward which Boris seemed to be

drawn by some unseen force. Loogo made a curt imperious gesture
and Boris knew that he had been commanded to take off his tunic.
This done and bare to the waist he faced the witch doctor and
this one painting swiftly, traced on the dazzling white hairless
breast of the young man, the symbol of death, a black skull. Then
they went out into the street, and the beating of the drums rose
almost to frenzy. The villagers had formed themselves into two
long lines. As the witch doctor and the Hungarian passed between
these, the lines closed in behind them and the whole village
moved toward the jungle, in a well ordered procession of nodding
plumes and shaking spears. The beating of the drums
Rose almost to a frenzy as they
disappeared into the jungle.

-16-

IV

In the midst of dark and still waters from which grew a
forest of the immense buttressed melancholy trees there was
a long and narrow turtleback of dry land. Here the tribe knelt
like worshippers in a cathedral, before a high alter that was
built with human skulls.

At strategic points, torces had been stuck in the ground.
On the alter itself was something that burned with a blue flame.
Dums spoke to each other in muffled whispers, but there was
always rhythm and from time to time this rhythm mysteriously
changed. The bodies of those who knelt swayed to the rhythm of
the drums. Plumed heads were bent. Hands were crossed upon
breasts. Before the high alter, with his back to what we may
perhaps call his congregation, stood the witch doctor. He stood
without motion. His face was turneed upward to the blue flame
on the alter. The focus of the entire scene was however the
skull embroidered with white feathers between the shoulders of
his black cloak.

Boris was not in evidence. Between the witch doctor and
those who knelt in the first row was an open apace. In this space
some tens of white doves cooed and hunted for seeds. Among the
doves, three from each side, came six little girls. They were so
young that even in that luxuriant climate their breast had not
yet begun to swell. They were garlanded with lovely flowers.
Their little black faces were very serious and solemn. They came
dancing with light and delicate steps. They were so bright in the

night, their eyes so shining, that they resembled fire-flys.

The witchdoctor turned and faced them. He made an upward gesture with his right hand and for a few moments the drums roared fortissimo.

Some of the drums were grouped. Some were solitary. Some were great. Some were small. Some were no more than a slotted cylinder of wood. Each crum had a percussive voice peculiar to itself. Sometimes the drums became a chorus. Sometimes one little drum spoke to a great drum and was answered. Drums which were near together seemed to speak in whispers. Those which were far apart spoke, each from its dark place, loud and clear. Here and there, caught in the light of a torch and turned upward and illumined by the full moon could be seen the face of a drummer. For the most part these drummers were strong men. They gleamed with sweat and although they had been drumming almost without cessation for hours and hours, they showed no signs of exhaustion. The expression on these faces varied with the rhythm of the moment. At times there was sweetness and tranquilty. At times frank savage excitement, but sometimes it seemed as if they were experiencing some sort of monstrous delight.

The drums, having roared in unison, became silent. Again the witch doctor lifted his right hand and the drums broke into a light syncopation that had about it a something innocent and gay. To these measures the six little girls danced in front of the alter.

Out of the darkness, at the rear of the worshippers, came Boris, his snow-white back in strong contrast to the dark brown and black bodies of those who swayed before the altar. Boris was carrying something in his arms, but only the witch doctor who faced

him could see what this was. As Boris moved slowly forward toward the witch doctor and the altar of skulls, the drum beats
smote the air more thickly and more loudly until almost it seemed
as if many lions were roaring.

Boris Odeschalchi knelt before the high priest and this one
took from his extended arms the little child of the missionary.
As he turned to lay her on the alter, it could be seen that she
was so frightened that she could not even scream. From the left
side of the altar came the old woman with the matted tray of
Pandanus leaves, upon which lay the knife, stained with the pure
blood of the dove. It seemed as if the drums amd the congregation
had gone demoniac, but when the witch doctor took up the knife in
his hand and helf it aloft so that it pointed at the moon, the
drums became silent. The wild bodies motionless as if frozen.

In that silence only the children moved and there could be
heard the light tappings of their little feet. They seemed to be
dancing a series of little geometric figures that became one thing
and then dissolved into another. As they danced, they lifted their
clear shrill voices in a kind of chant. Their voices broke upon
the silence like the voices of tree-frogs. Having completed their
evolutions three of the little girls danced off into the night at
one end of the altar and three into the night at the other.

The child had been laid on the high altar of skulls, just
below the blue flame. But the savage worshippers could no longer
see her because of the bodies of the high priest, and of Boris who
had risen to his feet. Boris and the witch doctor drew closer to
the child and it could be sensed that the latter was going to do
some awful thing with the knife.

198

-19-

A scream, too piercing, too pitiable, too shot with
terror to be described in words, broke the silence. Then, once
more the drums went into action. From a steady beating in groups
of six long beats, followed by two short ones, there developed
swiftly and with a crescendo that became tremendous rhythms too
complicated and exciting for a white ear to follow.

It is difficult to find words with which to describe what
followed. The congregation had come to their feet and it seemed
as if sanity had departed from them altogether. They danced and
contorted their bodies with the utmost conceivable demonstrations
of violence and they screamed at the tops of their lungs.

The sound of a drum even when it is tapped lightly, carries
far. When a well trained African band goes mad as on the present
occasion, the sound carries for miles and miles. The savages
beat upon the ground with their foreheads and the palms of their
hands. So also here and there in the dark forest, in far off and
isolated dwellings, wild people knew the meaning of the drumming
and moaned and screamed with excitement and knelt and pounded the
floor with their heads and hands. So also Bulbo, who had been
ordered to the punkah rope because the night was very hot, hearing
those drums became half mad with excitement, dropped the punkah
rope and beat upon the floor of the veranda with his hands and
his head.

Whenever Trelawney had been on the point of falling asleep,
the drums had prevented. What he thought and what he occasionally
said about black people in general and black drumming in particular
was not of an edifying nature. Indeed some of his explosions were
not fit to print. Suffock, always in an angry mood these days,

a young man who had been completely "gotten" by the climate,
had not even attempted to sleep. The little steamer that came up
the river once a month, and was even now tied at the wharf, had
brought a whole bag full of letters, magazines and newspapers.

A letter from his sister Maud [Mary], whom he loved dearly had given him surprise, pleasure and annoyance. It took very little to annoy him. Under separate cover she had sent him a copy of her latest photograph. He propped this against a pile of books on the table in front of him and as he looked at it his face softened. She was very beautiful, a tender lovely English face, like a flower. He thought her very lovely and in the same moment thought that if those drums didn't stop that mad rhythm, he would go mad. On the instant, each pore in his body opened wide and he went into a sudden drenching sweat and then he really did go mad for he saw that the punkah had stopped swinging. He rushed out on the veranda to find the maddened [frenzied] Bulbo beating the veranda floor with his head and hands. He kicked him savagely into attention.

"What are they doing?" he cried, "What are those drums saying?"

Bulbo shook his head repeatedly.

"Don't tell me you don't know, you black dog. I am going to know what you know if I have to choke it out of you. And he began to choke the negro with hands that in a frenzy over his anger, were as strong as steel. The negro was the bigger and the stronger man of the two, but he was not able to free himself. His eyes began to glaze over, he felt the approach of death and somehow managed to signify that he was now willing to tell. Suffolk freed the man's throat and Bulbo, after he had swallowed hard two or three times, said:

"Witch doctor makes sacrifice.

"It is not a goat this time," said Suffolk. "They don't make that much noise for a goat. Is this a human sacrifice? Is it a man?"

-27-

Bulbo shook his head.

"A woman?"

Again Bulbo shook his head.

"A child?"

This time Bulbo bowed his head as if he were terribly ashamed.

"I knew it," cried Suffolk, "~~that devil~~ Boris, that dirty monster! ~~but I'll get him,~~ so help me, I'll get him!"

He rushed back into the bungalow and took his automatic from a drawer in the writing table. At that moment Trelawney, curious about after the disturbance, on the verandah and ~~over~~ the high tones of Suffolk ~~on the veranda,~~ came out of his bedroom.

"Hey! Hey!," he said, "what are you going to do with that?"

"They are sacrificing a child, " said Suffolk, "and I know what child. Boris has let them do it. I knew it was going to happen. He kidnapped her. ~~When she was last seen, she was with him.~~ I am going to kill him."

"Oh no you aren't," said Trelawney cooly ~~cruelly~~, and with a sudden motion, quick as a snake striking, he snatched the automatic from the younger man's hand.

"You are not going to kill him for three good reasons," he said ~~said Trelawney~~, "the first is that if you went among those savages in their ~~that~~ present mood, they would tear you to pieces; the second reason is that you have no proof of any kind against Boris, and the third is that you are in my employ and subject to my orders and I order you to stop making a damn fool of yourself.

Perceiving that Suffolk was beginning to cool down, Trelawney patted him ~~Suffolk~~ affectionately on the shoulders and changed the subject.

At that moment, the frenzy of the drums ended and was followed by a death like silence. This in turn was broken by the

croaking of frogs and the shrill cry of a night bird. But the
swamps surrounding the island on which the alter of skulls had
been built, teemed with frogs and the voices of these rose in great
choruses and croakings, now hoarse and low, now shrill, and now
strong clarion and clear, almost like the notes of a braying jackass. There could be heard also the varied cries of many birds. Of
those who had witnessed the sacrificing of the missionary's child,
only Boris and Loogo remained. Into a bowl which contained a
dark liquid, blood perhaps, Loogo dipped the fore-finger of his
right hand and occasionally refreshing his supply of pigment, enclosed the black skull which he had already painted on the breast
of Boris with a broad dark circle.

Trelawney had gone back to bed to make another try for sleep
and Suffolk considerably calmer had finished going through his mail. The
photograph of his sister caught his eye, and he spoke to it.

"The idea! " he exclaimed, "you blithering little idiot! I
could break your damn neck for suggesting such a thing."

From his bedroom came the angry voice of Trelawney.

"Can't you let a man sleep! " he exclaimed. "Who are you
talking to now?"

"I'm talking to my damned fool sister,if you want to know,"
shouted Suffolk, once more ready to fly off the handle.

Trelawney came out of the bedroom, drew near the table,
picked up the photograph of Mary Suffolk, and looked at it.

"Is this your sister?" He asked.

"Yes," said Suffolk, "But she is a
damned little fool and if she had been here when I read her letter,
I'd have just about wring her neck.

-24-

"No really, " said Trelawney, "Whatever has the pretty creature been and gone and done?"

"Well, first of all, " said Suffolk, "She has engaged herself to marry Dr. Martin, The Dr. Martin."

"Well," said Trelawney, "Isn't that rather top-hole?"

"Righto," said Suffolk, "and then the blithering little idiot proposes to come here to this lousy fever hell hole to spend her honeymoon.

"That wouldn't be a good idea, would it," Said Trelawney, "Nothing fades so quickly in a climate like this as an english rose."

He glanced at his wrist-watch.

"I've done you an injustice," he said, "I seem to have slept for two hours, and that can only mean that for that unprecedented length of time, you have managed to keep your mouth shut."

"What time is it?" asked Suffolk

"Two o'clock," said Trelawney.

"I think," said Suffolk, " that I'll do a little turning in myself."

At that moment, with the slow measured tread, of booted feet, could be heard on the veranda

Note - their steps should be heard faintly at first, scrambling on the front path, & ranging on the verandah steps. The sequence should be emphasized into the later sequence of the steps of the feet.

25-A

But he did not at once do this. The sound of distant steps had caught his ear. He turned his head a little, the better to listen.

"There is Boris now, " he said.

The steps crunching on the gravel path could now be heard more clearly, but they were not even nor alike. One made a firm crisp sound and the other a shuffling sound. This difference was even more pronounced when the steps had mounted the veranda stair and moved along the veranda toward the door of the living room.

The two Englishmen started as if they had been guilty of
something and Boris Odeschalchi entered the room. The emotions
of the night had effected him profoundly. There was to begin with
the feeling that new and unheard of powers had been born in him.
In the second place he felt so fatigued and washed out that he had
no wish to exercise those powers. He wished of all things to fling
himself down on a bed and sleep. He had not expected to find the
Englishmen awake. and when Suffolk pointed an accusing finger at
him and said:

"I know what you have done. Bulbo told me and you are not
going to get away with it."

The Hungarian had a kind of liking for Suffolk, but no especial
respect for his mental and physical powers. If there was going to be
a scene he did not wish to be part of it.

"Suppose," he said, "we discuss all that after breakfast.
I am tired and if you don't mind too much, I am going to get some
sleep."

He moved toward the door of the bedroom, but Suffolk intervened.
Trelawney, who did not share the younger man's passions and prejudices
was frankly bored.

"You'd better get some sleep yourself," he said to Suffolk,
"and if you don't happen to wake up for a month, nobody would be the
worse for it."

It was as if Suffolk had not heard. His eyes were trying to
tear the truth from those of Boris'.

"You are beginning to be offensive," said this one. The
phrase and the contemptuous tone in which it was uttered were too
much for Suffolk. He clinched his fists and with the curious lack
of the knowledge of how to use them, which, like the inability to
swim is born in the average white man, made a furious swinging

lead with his right. The Hungarian ducked under this without
hurrying too much and as he did so, felt his temper rise. Perceiving
that the failure of the Englishman to land his swing had drawn him
off his balance and made of his right jaw an inviting target, the
temptation to hit proved irresistible. Boris had long shapely heavy
hands. His punch was like the kick of a mule. When Suffolk came to
and got to his knees, he had only an indistinct knowledge of what
had happened, but in his heart the unreasoning hate still burned.
He got to his feet and staggered to the writing table. He seemed to
lean on this for support like a drunken man; but as events almost
instantly proved, his mind had cleared and reasoned and reached a
definite and logical conclusion. He conceded that physically he was
no match for Boris, but the automatic which Trelawney had put back
in its drawer would swing the balance of power the other way. The
Hungarian in the meanwhile had shrugged his shoulders and turned to
Trelawney.

"I am sorry," he said, "but sooner or later he had to take one.
But I shouldn't have hit him. I ought to have taken down his breeches,
laid him across my knee and spanked hell out of him."

Suffolk had taken the automatic from the drawer and moved the
safety bolt from safe to ready.

"See how you like this one you dirty dog," he said.

Boris turned quickly and received a 45 caliber nickel coated
bullet in the exact center of his heart. If that heart had been
protected by an inch of armor plate, the mere impact of the bullet would
have knocked him down.

Trelawney knelt at once by the fallen man and in an instant
of time perceived that he was stone dead. He remained calm.

"How," he said coldly to Suffolk, "do you propose to square
yourself with the authorities?"

-2&-

Suffolk was a weak man. In pulling the trigger of the automatic, he had thought of himself as something noble and just, the young St. Michael overthrowing Lucifer. He no longer felt noble. He knew that in a moment or two he would be actively sick at his stomach and he shook with strongly pronounced jerking shakings like a man who has palsy; but without any knowledge of what he was doing, without any volition but that of instinct to do it, he returned the automatic to its accustomed drawer and shut this with a haste that amounted to violence.

There was a moment in during which, if either of the Englishmen had happened to be looking in that direction, the face of Bulbo, agog stare with fright and horror, might have been seen in the dark rectangle of the window.

"The best that you can hope for," said Trelawney, "if the law takes its course, is life imprisonment and if I were to go into the witness box and tell of the absolutely unprovoked and hideous thing that I have seen you do, you would hang."

"I say, old top," said Suffolk, his hands at his throat, "I say, old chap, don't talk that way. Great God man, can't you do something! Can't you get me out of this? I tell you I can't go to prison. I'd sooner kill myself."

"Well," said Trelawney quietly, and if a stone could speak, it would have just such a voice, "there ought to be at least eight more cartridges in that pistol of yours and one of them, if you aim right and don't flinch, ought to do the trick."

But Suffolk's threat to take his own life had no more meaning than the usual talk of suicide. He did instead a thing far more shocking. He burst into tears and dropped to his knees at Trelawney's feet and made the sounds, mostly inarticulate of a little child that is in horrible trouble.

"Pull yourself together," said Trelawney, still cold as ice,
"~~You are so useful to me in some ways that I am going to lie for~~
~~you.~~ If questions are asked, Boris, in a delirium of malaria, shot
himself. If no questions are asked he has simply disappeared. If
you don't pull yourself together at once I shall lose my temper
and break every bone in your body. Going to be sick are you? Better
take yourself *out beyond the* ~~and your vomit to the~~ veranda rail."

While Suffolk was at the business of being sick over the veranda
rail Trelawney straightened the arms and legs of the dead man and
brought from behind the curtain in the corner of the room two of the
long handled shovels which are used for digging post holes. ¶They
dug the grave behind some hibiscus bushes in a corner of the compound.
The moon now low in the heavens watched the burial from the beginning
to the end. The frogs in the river and swamps made sounds which were
neither dolorous nor merry. The moon watched all the time. She
saw the dead man half carried and half dragged from the bungalow to
the appointed spot. She saw the whole digging of the shallow grave.
She would have given Trelawney most of the credit for the celerity
of the accomplishment, for every now and then Suffolk had to drop his
shovel and *be* ~~by~~ sick. She saw them lower the body of Boris Odeschalchi
into the grave. She saw Trelawney cross his hands upon his breast,
but it is doubtful if she heard his attempts to remember some of the
tremendous phrases from the service which the Church of England prescribes for the burial of the dead.

"'I am the resurrection and the life,'" he said, and after getting
all mixed up in *the part in* which the grave is asked to describe the exact location of its victory and death is denied its sting, he recalled
only that "Man *that* ~~who~~ is born of woman hath but a little time to live."

-30-

The moon saw the filling in of the grave and the punctilious effort

of the two Englishmen to make the freshly stirred earth look no

different from the hard and trampled earth surrounding it. But from

a post behind the hibiscus bushes, the negro, Bulbo, looked on only

long enough to fix the exact location of the grave in his rudimentary

mind.   He then stole away, silent as a shadow until he had made a

safe offing. Then he broke into the long strided swift graceful and

contained gate of the born runner. As straightly as the needle heads

for the magnetic pole, so straightly did Bulbo steer for the house

of the medicine man.

The Englishmen returned to the bungalow and Trelawney shot half

a grain of morphine into the upper arm ~~shoulder~~ of the hysterical Suffolk. The

morphine quieted Suffolk's nerves a little but did not make him sleepy.

He walked the length of the room again and again. Trelawney had no

thought of sleep either. He sat in the easiest of the chairs and

smoked innumerable cigarettes.

Once more, with only the light of the low hanging moon and the

blue fire, Loogo, the witch doctor stood before the altar of skulls.

But this time the body which lay on the altar just below the fire was

not that of the missionary's child. It was the body of Boris Odeschalchi.

The face and hands and his the crumpled white suit were stained with earth.

The medicine man with the doctor spoke to the dead man in quick urgent tones. At the

same time he kept clinching and unclinching his hands. As he clinched

them he brought them forward and inward in a powerful gesture of urgency.

So, you have seen a man at the race track making an unconscious effort

to encourage the horse, upon which he has placed his money, to greater

exertions, to the one last desperate necessary burst of speed. Upon

the knitted brows and the commanding face of the witch doctor was an

expression of concentration so powerful that it amounted to tortment. He

was urging the dead man to come back. He was insisting upon it. He

~~88-A~~

The tribe, with the exception of one torch bearer who stood beside the witch doctor and the dancing girl who knelt near him and facing him, had departed. Between them, face upward, lay the body of Boris Odeschalchi. The face and hands and the crumpled white suit were stained with earth. The witch doctor spoke to the dancing girl in quick urgent tones and she in similar tones seemed to speak to the dead man. Presently however, she unbuttoned the dead man's tunic and laid her left hand over his heart. She laid her right hand over her own heart. At this the witch doctor began to clinch and unclinch his hands. As he clinched them he brought them forward and inward in a gesture of powerful urgency. So you may have seen a man at the race track making an unconscious effort to encourage the horse, upon which he had placed his money, to greater exertions, to the one last desperate necessary burst of speed. Upon the knitted brows of the commanding face of the witch doctor was an expression of concentration so powerful that it amounted to torment. He was urging the dead man to come back. He was urging the warm vital current which controls locomotion to pass from the body of the dancing girl into that of the dead man. But the dead man lay still and his wide open eyes were glazed and dead.

~~"Come back, " he said in powerful tones, "Come back."~~

The dancing girl leaned closer and closer to the body. She leaned until the back of her right hand, which covered her own heart, touched the back of the left hand which covered the dead heart of Boris. During this ceremony the witch doctor seemed to redouble in concentration and urgency. But the dead man continued to lie still and dead.

The witch doctor spoke an order in native to the torch bearer and this one laid down the torch at the side of the body so that the face which had been brightly lighted was now in shadow.

Then once more the witch doctor urged the dead man to come back.

"Come back! Come Back! Boris Odeschaloff," he said, "~~Come back! Come Back!~~"

It could be seen that something was beginning to happen in the shadow. A kind of fluttering and a struggling. The torch bearer lifted the torch from the ground and it could be seen that the dead body was struggling upward into a sitting position. The witch doctor rose and helped the dead man to his feet.

"Easy, easy," he said, "you will be stronger in a minute."

212

-33--33-

A yellow fog had come over the Thames river from the sea and invaded the great city of London. It was a fog of varying densities. It varied from light mist to a watery opaqueness. You could see for instance the dome of St. Paul Cathedral, but not in the body of the church the Cleopatra Needle was visible. The tower of London was not. About the Sackville Club the fog was so dense that the members could not see out of the windows. An American caught in such a fog could not have been stopped from talking about it. To an Englishman it was however only a very usual climatic condition. Mortimer Johnson stood in front of the coal fire in the club library and warmed his back and read a newspaper. There were several other readers in the room.

On the chimney breast above Mr. Johnson's head was a bronze plaque in which was carved the latin word for silence. In spite of this warning Mr. Johnson was so interested and intrigued by an item which had caught his eye that he could not refrain from expressing these feelings out loud.

"By jove! " he said, "Now I say! Now really! "

A fragile old gentleman put down his own newspaper and joined Mr. Johnson in front of the fireplace.

"Did you see this bit sir?," asked Mr. Johnson, and before the old man could answer, two other members impelled by curiosity came forward.

"It is the first time it has ever happened in history," said Mr. Johnson.

"The first time that what has ever happened?" asked the old man.

"The first time that a shark has followed a ship all the way across the ocean and this time it wasn't only one shark. It was hundreds of sharks, thousands of them. The Londonerry, sailing

from Wamba on the west coast of Africa docked this morning at the
King George dock. Her ~~ship~~ captain reports that he had no sooner
made his offing and rung for full speed ahead ~~than the~~ when sharks
began to appear in the wake of the vessel. They followed him clear
to the mouth of the Thames and half way up the river."

"There must have been a dead man on board," said the old man,
Sailors believe that when there is a dead man on a ship, sharks
follow that ship in the hope that the dead man will be thrown over
to them.

that's just what the
"That's the funny part of it," interrupted Johnson excitedly.
~~captain said~~ ~~there was a~~ corpse aboard
~~There wasn't any dead man on the ship~~ And they don't
~~even a book even the poor old chap been dead~~

If the club members had happened to be in a certain distant
part of London, they might have seen going through a narrow street
in whic mist drifted, the dead body of Boris Odeschalchi followed
                                         its
at a respectful distance by ~~his~~ servant Loogo, the witch doctor.
¶The house in which the beautiful Maud Suffolk lived with her father
and mother and thought often,with deep interest and affection of her
brother over the seas in dark Africa, was pure Adams, except that
there had been added certain deeper and softer pieces of modern
furniture for the sake of comfort. The mantelpiece was of a soft
yellow marble into which had been let medallions in blue and white,
made by the famous Mr. Wedgewood after th classic designs by the
equally famous Mr. Flaxman.

By the afternoon post,Maud had received a letter from her
brother which had greatly disturbed her. She had read it over a
                                   cursed
number of times.and had ~~discribed~~ its contents with both her parents
                                                      Arthur
and now she had been reading it to her fiancé, Dr. ~~Martin~~,who had
dropped in on his way home from the hospital. Dr. Martin, a tall
strong smooth-shaven immaculately tailored man of forty, now held the
                   his
letter in ~~her~~ hands. He had been reasoning with her and trying

to calm her.

"But," she said, "Such a strange mad letter. It isn't in the least like ~~Jeffrey~~ my brother." [its]

"The passage," said Dr. Martin," In which he forbids his charming sister to spend her honeymoon in a fever swamp is clear enough."

"Yes," said the girl, "But there are passages which I don't understand at all. What does he mean about ~~the dead comes back~~ a country where ~~and walk about the earth as living dead things?~~ ~~until there is no longer any room for the living?~~" [to life]

Dr. Martin smiled in a cool quizzical way. "I am sure I don't know," he said.

"I have felt so queer since the letter came," said she. " I feel as if something were trying to invade my personality and destroy its integrity, and I am so worried about Jeffrey. Darling, you don't think, you don't think that by any chance my poor brother is going---Mad?"

The doctor opened his arms and she went into them like a homing pigeon.

"Of course I don't," he said, "And you must stop feeling queer."

He kissed her on the mouth with great sweetness and tenderness.

"Forget about Jeffrey," he said, "Forget about all the ~~little~~ things that are bothering you. Don't do anything but love me!"

Again he kissed her and the little Adam's clock on the mantel-piece chimed the hour.

" I must go get dressed," he said, "Or we shall be late."

"I wish we didn't have to go," she said. "They are all old friends and dear friends, but I don't want anyone but you my sweet,·· my dear."

Boris and the witch doctor had taken a modest suite of rooms

215

-36-

on Jermyn Street. The rooms were above a grocery store which
proudly flaunted the statement that it was a grocery story by
the permission of his Gracious Majesty, the King, and displayed
the royal arms, supported by a handsome Lion and Univorn in color
and gilt.

Boris was seated in a chair, as dead as an Egyptian
carving. Loogo knelt in front of the fireplace. In this was a
grate and a glowing fire, cannel coal. From a black bag reminiscent
of Africa Loogo was taking the photograph of Mary Suffolk and the
letter which she had written to her brother. He had taken also
the skulls of three monkeys and other paraphenalia of magic.
Lastly, a powder which when thrown on the fire burned with a
strong blue flame. He had addressed himself to the monkey skulls
in African but to the photograph which he presently took in his
two hands he did not at first speak at all. It seemed as if he
were undergoing some strong convulsion of the spirit. You had
the feeling that he was trying to force his spirit into the
inanimate photograph. Or possibly, through the medium of the
photograph he was trying to force his spirit into the living
girl. At moments, it actually seemed as if the masses which
went to make up the lovely shadowed image of the girl were
actually moving and working. The eyes of the witch doctor blazed.
Presently he laid himself flat down on the floor, clasping the
photograph to his breast and became motionless. It could be seen
that in the blazing eyes the light was beginning to die. The
light dies altogether. He might have been another dead man.

Mary suffolk had finished dressing for the dinner-
dance and was being admired by her mother.

"My darling," said Mrs. Suffolk, "You look perfectly
lovely, but...."

"What is the matter?" asked Mary.

"There is a runner in your left stocking," said her mother crisply.

Aut "When I shall just have to run and change them, but I hate to keep my darling waiting." *a I hate to keep Arthur waiting* *thats the second pair this week!*

Mary ran into her dressing room, selected a fresh pair of stockings and sat down to put them on. She pulled up her pretty frock as much as was necessary and had almost completed the change when she noticed that the great black family cat, Niger, suddenly arched his back as if in fear and defiance, and spat. At the same moment, Mary had a feeling that she was not alone in the room and she hastily pulled down her dress. She rose to her feet and looked

-37- 38

behind her. There was no one. She had a sensation of nausea. And
then she seemed to hear a voice. Where this voice came from she
did not know but the feeling that someone was speaking to her was
so strong and she was so startled that she spoke back.

"You'll come to me?" she said, "You will come to me? Who are you?"

A door between the dressing room and the bedroom where Maud's
mother waited was ajar. Hearing her daughter apparently carrying on
a conversation with someone, Mrs. Suffolk came into the dressing room
and seeing no one to whom Maud's words could have been addressed, very
naturally said:

"Whom are you talking to?"

Miss Suffolk's nerves were badly shaken but she managed to keep her
self-possession.

"I actually thought," said she, "That somebody really spoke to
me. It was so real that before I knew it, I had answered. Mother
dear, look at Niger."

Niger had once more arched his back, but his fear and animosity
seemed now to be directed at Maud herself.

"Oh mother dear," Said Maud, "Everything has been so queer today,
ever since Jeffrey's letter."

Forget about Jeffrey's letter, my precious," said her mother,
"and run along to your young man and have a beautiful time.

"I feel so queer," said Maud. "Every now and then I have had the
feeling that I was not really myself and that I was trying to be someone else. It is a horrible feeling."

The witch doctor had risen from the floor and had finished
laying out full evening-dress for his dead master. He now laid himself down comfortably on the lounge and with hardly any effort at all
succeeded in animating the dead man and becoming himself, to all

39

intents and purposes, lifeless. The dead man's eyes began to
blaze. He rose to his feet and began to undress.

In spite of her wish to be alone,with Dr. Martin, Maud had
almost enjoyed the dinner and now when she was dancing and in her
lover's arms, she felt almost secure. But during the dinner,it had
happened that twice she had caught herself with that horrible feeling
of trying to be someone else and now just as the dance finished and
the young lady at the piano pretended to be in an exhausted state,
the feeling came over her again. And a part of the feeling was an
urge which drew her eyes to the stately row of french windows which
formed one whole side of the room.

Daniel Quickley, an old friend and admirer of Maud's happened
to notice a curious expression of alarm and bewilderment that had
come over her face and remarked to his late dancing partner,

"I wonder what's the matter with Maud. She looks happy enough
when she is dancing with that long legged lover of hers, but the moment
she stops, she goes white and looks as if she was seeing things."

"Nothing but nerves dear boy," said his partner, "If you were
a pure young girl,rather religious and decidedly spiritual, and you
knew that the day after tomorrow night you would be alone in some
hotel bedroom at the mercy of an amorous man, you would be nervous."

The mist drifted lightly past the french windows and out of this
mist loomed Boris Odeschalchi. For a moment his blazing eyes held
hers. The mist thickened and he vanished. She gasped and with a
violent effort at self-control, forced a smile to her lips, leaned
toward the girl on the piano seat and said:

"Darling, please don't stop. I want to dance."

"Darling," said the girl on the piano seat, and she lifted her
hands and pretended that there was no longer any life in her fingers.
"I am done in," she said.

40

A young man seated himself on the extreme end of the piano seat and said:

"If you won't play, You'll sing, and you'll jolly well like it. Move over! "

The girl moved further along the seat. The young man moved to the center of it and his strong able fingers began to crash out the opening chords of "You'll take the high road and I'll take the low road." And the girl began to sing in a loud sweet clear gipsy explike voice.

Dr. Martin noticed his sweethear's pallor.

"You are white as a sheet," he said, "I will go fetch you a glass of champagne."

"Don't leave me," she said quickly.

But he had turned away and did not hear her.

Maud hesitated a moment and then, unobserved by the others, who had clustered around the piano to see just how much noise they could possibly make, walked quickly to one of the french windows, opened it, stepped out on theterrace and closed the window behind her. ¶At a little distance, in a lovely old garden of clipped Yew, half hidden in mist, she saw Boris Odeschalchi ~~sitting on a long bench of white marble~~. She walked slowly toward him.

When Dr. Martin returned with the glass of champagne, he did not see her anywhere and he whispered to a pretty little girl with a pug nose:

"I say Myrtle; what's become of Maud?"

"If you must know," said Myrtle, who was a born tease, "I think it highly probably that she has rushed off somewhere or other to powder her nose."

Maud had sunk down on the marble bench beside Boris, but at a little distance from him.

-44-

"I don't know why I came to you," she said in her clear beautiful english voice. "I don't know why I sit here and let you talk to me about the dead, ~~coming back.~~"

"Because," said the dead man, but in the unmistakable voice of the witch doctor, "The dead will come back."

His eyes blazed into hers and drew closer to them.

"You came to me," he said, "Because you could not help yourself, ~~and now where I am going, you will follow.~~" *You are going to assist me in ~~returning~~ the dead to those who ~~had loved them~~.*

The girl had stiffened her shoulders but these now relaxed. It looked for a moment as if she were going to collapse. Boris Odeschalchi rose and walked off into the fog. When he was at a little distance, *He stoped looked back.* Maud Suffolk rose and followed him. The fog thickened about them and they vanished.

Since Maud Suffolk's mysterious disappearance, four days and nights had passed. Her mother was half mad with insomnia and anxiety. The narcotics which Dr. Martin had prescribed had had no effect.

"But my darling," said her husband, taking her in his arms, "We are doing everything that is possible. ~~Every man, women and child in England is hunting for her.~~ I myself have thought of something which may just possibly help us to find a clue. After I have dropped our good doctor at the hospital, I am going straight to Scotland Yard to talk with Inspector Priestly.

"Now you keep a stiff upper-lip,"

"And you are to lie down," said Dr. Martin, "And *you are to* take two of the tablets. They are bound to work, they must."

Dr. Martin himself looked horribly the worse for wear. It was very difficult for him to hold staunchly to his professional manner. *Mrs Suffolk tried to be brave and contained. The aeroen passed them to the door of the living room, and said: "God luck to you both. You are dear, dear boys..."*

-42-

In a suburb of London in the midst of old dilapidated
grounds and lawns which had not been trimmed, stood a gloomy three-
story house in the Georgian manner. The house had not been occupied for many years. In the cellars, under it, dating to a
previous century, much of the house's furnishings had been stored.
There was a confusion of chairs, tables, packingcases, etc. Near
the foot of a flight of stone stairs, worn hollow by generations
of feet, knelt Loogo, the witch doctor. Opposite him knelt Mary
Suffolk. At one side of her stood Boris Odelosi, holding a tall
altar candle. Between Mary Suffolk and the witch doctor lay the
body of a dead man. His hair was gray. He looked to have been the
head of a middle class family.

The scene recalled that earlier one in Africa when Boris
himself had been brought back to a semblance of life. Only on this
occasion, Boris was the torch bearer and the part of the dancing
girl was being acted by Mary Suffolk. The witch doctor exerted
his will and urged the dead man to come back. He opened the
dead man's shirt and when this was opened Mary Suffolk at the witch
doctor's command laid her left hand over the dead man's heart.
She laid her right hand over her own heart and then leaned closer
to the dead man, and closer until the backs of her hands touched.

At a signal from the witch doctor, Boris shifted the
altar candle so that his dead body came between it and the face of
the other dead man.

The witch doctor seemed to redouble in energy and power.
He kept clinching and unclinching his hands in the well-remembered
gesture of urgency as if with everything that he had that was
either physical or mental he was trying to force someone else
to do something which he resisted doing.

In the darkness something seemed to be happening.
Once more Boris shifted the candle and it could be seen that the
dead man had struggled into a sitting position. The witch doctor
helped him to his feet and supported him until he had achieved
a sense of balance and could stand alone. The witch doctor turned
to Mary Suffolk, ~~who had also risen to her feet. Maximax~~

She looked to be only half-conscious. He spoke to
her softly and gently:

"Again," he said, "you have helped to bring one back.
It is easier for you now. You are leaning very fast. See! Now
he can stand alone. He has no brain. His heart does not beat.
Yet, he stands on his feet. He can walk and he will find his
way straight to his old home and to those who think that they
still love him."

While he spoke, Mary Suffolk seemed to be coming out
of her trance, to understand what was being said to her.

Without thinking, perhaps, the witch doctor had for a
moment loosened his control over Mary Suffolk's mind. A partial,
perhaps a complete realization of the horrible thing which she had
helped do came over her. She gave one look at the man whom she had
just helped to bring back, gave one piercing scream, ran swiftly
to the flight of stone steps and up them.

The witch doctor watched her curiously but made no attempt
to check her flight or to pursue. He turned to the man who had
just been brought back, ~~said:~~

"~~Now, you.~~"

The dead man walked ob~~stinately and~~ a little fumblingly
toward the flight of steps and went up them. The witch doctor
looked intently at the flame of the candle which Boris was carrying and the flame went out. At first, nothing could been seen in

the darkness but the two blazing eyes of the witch doctor. They
resembled the eyes of a great cat. But presently the white face
of Boris could be seen faintly and glimmeringly. He was following
the witch doctor toward the stair.

Mary Suffolk's father and inspector Priestly,of Scotland
Yard, had been talking for half an hour in the latter's office.

"Please don't misunderstand me", said Mr. Suffolk, in
his gentle voice, "I don't mean that I actually believe in ghosts
and that sort of thing but to a certain extent I am what is called
'psychic'. Several times I have had a presentiment that a certain
thing was going to happen and it has heppened. In these ways,
my daughter is very much like me. So, you see, she felt this
presence in the room and felt it so strongly that when the voice
spoke to her she answered. Is it possible that somebody at a
distance succeeded in influencing my daughter?"

"Sometimes," said inspector Priestly, "I think that
anything is possible."

"The Occult,"continued Mr. Suffolk, " must sound like
the sheerest nonsense to most of the clever, practical man connected with Scotland Yard, and I am very grateful for the sympathetic way in which you have listened to me, and I do think that
it may be easier for you to find my daughter now that you have
more precise knowledge of her character."

"It may," said the inspector. "Let us hope so."

Through the fog and mists, Mary Suffolk, half ran, half
walked, without any objective. Almost she gave the impression of a
wounded bird fluttering,and indeed, she had been wounded and
most grievously. The realization had come to her proud sensitive
religious soul that she had been compelled to take part in horrible

and unforgivable rites. She believed in Heaven and Hell.
She believed herself to be one of the damned. The mist cleared
and she found herself in front of a small Gothic Church. She went
in. The place was lighted only by groups of candles which burned
in front of Saints. From the rose window above the Gothic arch
by which she had entered, colored light whose source must have
been a powerful arc lamp in the street without, entered the place
and picked up various details of architecture. She turned and looked
upward at this window. In the midst of it, a medieval Christ had
been nailed upon a cross. Knights in armor and quaint ladies in
fourteenth century costumes crowded about the feet of the cross.
The two thieves and various Christian symbols filled the sides and
above was a great long narrow eye. Perhaps it was intended to be
that of God, the Father. Mary Suffolk, without knowing what she
was doing, spread out her arms as if she,too,were being crucified.

"Merciful Father," she cried, "What have I done?
What have I done? Is there no forgiveness?"

In the parlor of a small tasteless middle class house,
the Reverend Father Richard Bentley together with his sweet-faced
sister, a nun of the Urseline Order, were trying to console their
mother. She was all in black. Her face was red and swollen with
weeping. She wore an old-fashioned bonnet with long heavy streamers
of crepe. That day she had buried her husband and she could not
reconcile herself to the fact that her beloved was no longer in the
house and would never again be in the house.

"That may well be," said the mother, "But I have given
to His Service my two children   and now they have
taken all that I have left me. We have laid your dear father in
his grave. I shall never see him again. It isn't fair! I loved
him and I want him. Wherever I look there is something to remind

me of him and to wring my heart."

The nun with the sweet face said, "Come, mother
darling."

The mother turned up her face so the son could kiss
her and started obediently for the door but turned and began
as it seemed to weep all over again.

"How," she said, "can I bear to ~~look at~~ *look at* that chair,"
and she pointed to a very usual and rather comfortable-looking
arm chair by the side of the table on which there was a lamp,
"he always sat in that chair and now it will always be empty.
See, there on the table beside it is his pipe. I shall never
again see him sitting in that chair and reaching for his pipe."

She began to sob and her daughter lead her from the
room. The priest remained alone in the room, sad and thoughtful.

Presently the door into the hall opened quietly
and the priest's father, the man whom he had that very day helped
to bury, walked into the room and sat down. His eyes were dead
eyes and there was no expression on his face. He looked as if he
was made of wax. The priest perhaps trembled for a moment. It
is sure that he crossed himself, but the voice in which he spoke
to the dead man was clear and natural.

"Your spirit has been sent back to us, father," he
said, "Have you come to guide us, to watch over us? Is there, per-
paps, something that we are to do for you?"

The dead man, of course, did not answer. The priest
approached closer to the body of his father.

"~~Aren't you going~~ *Can I help you* to speak to me?" he said, and then
as he drew still closer to the corpse his hand must have touched
it's ~~hand became~~ he said suddenly, "I thought you were a spirit

-47-

but you are not you ~~your~~ fall

~~but your hand is as cold as ice."~~

He felt for signs of life but found none. The heart had no pulse, the breast did not rise and fall. The eyes were dead. It had not been difficult for the aesthetic to believe that the spirit of his father had entered the house but that which sat in the chair was no spirit. It was a corpse. Above the brows of the corpse he made the sign of the cross and then, turning his face upward, "I ask" he said, "for guidance - for understanding. ~~What am I to do? We loved him. We wanted him and now he has come back.~~ Merciful Father, teach me what I should do!"

There was a kind of gasping sound. The priest turned and saw that his sister had returned. He stepped quickly to her ~~side~~ and said, "Don't be frightened. ~~What has happened is utterly beyond knowledge and experience."~~

"But," said the nun, "It's father's spirit."

"No, my dear," he said, "It's not our father's spirit. It is only his body. The heart does not beat; the breath come and go. ~~He is cold like ice and yet he walked into this room and sat down on that chair. Let's go where we can talk..."~~ Taking hold of his sisters arm He ~~and~~ they moved into the hall ~~of the house and~~ closed the door between themselves and the dead man.

There, the priest continued, "We loved him - we wanted him. He came back and now...there is no place for him."

The priest's voice, hitherto in fine control, broke nervously ~~and harsher~~ and became higher and shriller, "Now," he repeated, "We don't want him. "

"Ssh", said the nun, "Mother will hear you. Mother mustn't know."

227

-46-

A policeman saw a woman struggling and swaying in the mist.
He saw her sway into an entry, and clutch at the wall for support
and sink in a heap to the pavement. He hurried to her side, flashing
a torch. He saw that her hands were bleeding. He saw that the palms
had been pierced as if some blunt instrument had been driven through
them. Instinctively he looked down at her feet. The insteps of these
had been pierced in a like manner.

He blew and blew his whistle. Presently in every direction,
footsteps could be heard ringing on pavements. A little crowd gathered

"My Gawd," said one voice.

"It looks like she had been nailed to something,"

A cockney voice cried," I tell you she has been crucified."

Maud Suffolk lay upon a bed in a private room of the ~~city~~
hospital. ~~Her bed was surrounded by physicians and surgeons.~~ But
one man ~~older~~ and very much older than the others did not seem to
belong to either of these professions. ~~Nor was he any kind.~~
He was a spidery little man with a face which resembled that of a
monkey. He was almost a hunch-back. He talked with great quickness
and precision. You had the feeling that he was always sure that he
was right. He wore a black Inverness cape fastened at the throat
by two links of steel chain. His white hair stood well out from
his head. ~~He had a short white beard that bristled in the same way.~~

The lovely girl upon whom were the marks of the Stigmata was
unconscious. Dr. Martin slowly removed the dressings from her
wounded hands.

"I think you were right, Lord Avon," he said, "I believe that
you who are neither a physician or a surgeon are the one man in the
world best able to solve this mystery."

46

228

X X X X t

(Middle of page 46-)

Taken to a private room in the Emergency Hospital, Maud Suffolk lay
silently upon her bed. Bandages had been drawn about her torn hands and feet. Her
suffering had stilled her so she was undisturbed by the tense talk around her.

A group of alert, shrewd and forceful men, the foremost doctors of London,
surrounded her bed. Dominating them was a little man with a body so tense and electric
it seemed twisted. His bright eyes behind thick lenses had a strange brilliancy as
though they had looked upon forces unfamiliar to the average eye. He was Professor
von Haeckelmetz, the foremost philosopher and student of occult lore in Europe. His
age had gone on almost into the ageless, so superior in wisdom and experience was he to
even the oldest of these veteran doctors and scientists. His black Inverness cape
was thrown across his lap. His white hair stood well out from his head. And his talk
was inthe quick precise tones of challenge and debate:

".....your Science! .....Gentlemen, there are things greater than your
books....things beyond your Science. There are forces....enormous forces that
we do not understand------ "

Here they interrupted him protesting:\" But Professor von Haeckelmetz,
you don't mean.....not in this day...that a supernatural power caused these wounds!
That is childish----"

At the word "childish", the strange little Professor was on his feet
challenging them: " Childish-----Gentlemen, I think we are going to find that this one
wound was not made by an iron spike! I think that this wound and the one through her right
hand and those through her feet were not drilled by any material agencies. I think they
have been drilled by some awful and contrite thought."

"By a what? " snapped one of the younger doctors.

" A thought " said Professor von Haeckelmetz, tapping his forehead.

And then using tone and gesture to make his statement even more impressive,
he added: " Gentlemen, what you are seeing here is one of the strangest manifestations

...2

of the human body and the human soul.... it is the STIGMATA. "

A murmur of protest came from all parts of the group.

" Is there one among you who has ever seen anything like this? " the Professor
asked. The men in the group shook their heads.

" But I have " said the little Professor. " There have been several cases,
reported in various parts of the world again and again. Honorable and intelligent
men have examined them, and have testified to the facts. And the Church, approaching
these cases with the utmost caution, with the most complete research, have accepted them
as truths that can not be denied.

" Such wounds have come to sensitive persons like this beautiful girl lying here.
Some great emotional shock has come upon her. Some demonic force may have attacked
her. And in her struggle for spiritual purity, to cleanse herself from some foul
impulse that may have assailed her, she has cried out with all her despairing strength....
and Gentlemen, these wounds have opened, wounds that are immortal in their significance."

Here the Professor turned to the girl, directing one of the other doctors to
bare the girl's right hand.

As the bandage is released, the blood wells up into the palm; and the
Professor asks an elderly and very famous Doctor: " How long do you think it will take
for these wounds to heal?

"From ten days to three weeks."

"Good " said the Professor, " now we shall have our test. Your science says
from ten days to three weeks. I say these wounds will heal within three days of the
time they first appear. So I have observed in such cases; and that time , Gentlemen,
is now nearly past."

The startled looks in the faces of the doctors turned the Professor's
attention to the girl, and all stood tensely witnessing an amazing change. The fresh
blood had ceased its flow.

"Come close...everyone ", the Professor commanded.

....3

The astonished savants bent over ~~Maud~~ Mary Suffolk to watch the strange activity.
All blood had disappeared from the wound.   Slowly the torn flesh seemed to draw together
The dreadful hole in the tender palm seemed to fill with firm tissue.

The professor turned to the awed group: " You see, Gentlemen,.....a force
beyond your Science."

Before the disconcerted men of learning could begin to argue and compare, their
comments ~~were~~ they stopped by a sharp change that had struck intothis girl who had just
now been so lovely and so quiet.   Dr. Martin moved impulsively to her side.

~~Maud~~ Mary Suffolk struggled as though contending with some terrific force that was
thrusting itself upom her.   Her deep g sps and wrenching movements told the doctors
of the extreme effort she was making to defend herself against the power that was
attacking her.

Then a great trembling shock her body, the desperate commotion of being
overcome. Her forhead lowered into wrinkles. Her eyes toon on a sharp and cunning and
penetrating hardness. Her mouth ~~wrinkled~~ writhed with an evil vigor.

She began to speak, at first in low mutterings as though still resisting, and
then with sharp incisive tones.

While the others stared, unable to comprehend what was happening, the little
professor moved hastily nearer to her head, bending over so he would miss no word.
He was excited with the terrible importance of what might be spoken.

Then from the face that had been so round and girlish came the ominous voice
of the Jungle, the voice of the Witch-doctor, saying: THE GRAVE WILL GIVE UP ITS
OWN, UNTIL THE WORLD WILL BE FILLED WITH THE WALKING DEAD."

Horrified by this voice coming from the girl he loved, Dr. Martin cried out:
" That's not her voice.....it's someone else.....it's not ~~Maud~~ Mary."

" Of course not " said the Professor, sympathizing with Dr. Martin's
anguish. She is pressed with some unholy occult power.

Then he turned to the others, his voice vibrant with excitement as he said:

....4--

" Gentlemen....you heard that! .....there is our secret..there is our connection with these living dead."

The girl, spent by her exertions, had dropped back against the pillows. Leaving *and* to the care of Dr. Martin, Professor von Haeckelmetz summoned the others from the room with a soft but significant tone: " Come....Gentlemen....come....."

Soon all London was throbbing with terror at the presence of these living dead. The newspapers cried out more news of the shocking tragedy in each new edition. The horror of these lifeless beings who were walking among the living had aroused the city and the nation.

In another room in the hospital, a council of the gravest importance had been called. High state officials, the heads of the Police Department, the foremost scientists and doctors were present.

A committee of doctors has just finished examining two specimens of the walking dead. One is a woman, the other is a man.

Professor von Haeckelmetz sits to one side , in the center of a small group of national leaders. The doctors have been whispering together in final consultation, their faces and manners revealing their complete bafflement.

The alert little Professor who has fought their scepticism so long, now calls to the doctors: " You gentlemen of the Medical Science....if you are ready now---"

The doctors come to the Professor and the officials, and again the Professor inquires: " Gentlemen..have you come to anything--------?"

Bewildered, they admit they have reached no explanation, for these two beings are dead....no evidence of animation...no response to tests for life.

The little Professor stands and with characteristic gestures, speaks to them: " Gentlemen, you will admit there is nothing known to Medical Science that can release Rigor Mortis.....nothing that can stop decomposition. Yet you have these beings before you. Gentlemen, only when you believe in the Occult can this be

232

....5

explained....nothing but the Occult could accomplish this.   Unless we find the seat of t
this evil influence---as this poor girl who is a defenseless agent has told us----this
City of London is going to be over-run with the dead.   And the living: they will go
insane; they will kill themselves.   And at night, ⌐ʀxɪsɴsɴ, the families who have
buried their loved ones that day will sit around in mortal terror lest their dead
stalk back into their midst.   ⌐entlemen, unless this unholy occult force is
stopped, CIVILIZATION IS DOOMED! "

-51-

When Mary Suffolk had sufficiently recovered from the shock to which she had been subjected she was taken home. Here, her physical condition improved slowly but she was in a mental state which drove Doctor Martin, because he could find no way to remedy it, almost too desperate and which furnished Von Hecklemetz a magnificent field for inquiry into the Occult. Both men were frequent visitors.

Late one afternoon, Mary was resting in a deep chair. Her lover had drawn his chair close to hers and held one of her hands frankly in both of his. Von Hecklemetz flitted and darted about the room. He seemed possessed with an untiring energy and spirit of inquiry. He would plant himself directly in front of Mary, ask her one or more leading questions and would then dart away almost like a bird that had stolen something, while he appeared to digest her answers.

"Do you now have the feeling," he asked, "that this evil spirit can take possession of you whenever it wishes?"

"Yes" she said simply. "I no longer try to resist."

"Do you feel the presence before it possesses you?"

"Yes."

"Can you fight it?"

"No."

"When your own spirit comes back to you, you always find yourself kneeling in front of this black man?"

"Yes." she said.

"At this moment do you feel that you are your own normal self?"

"I shall never again," she answered, "be my normal self. How can I be! The horror of what is happening to me is too great."

-52-

While Von Hecklemetz darted off to digest these answers,

Doctor Martin leaned down and touched Mary's hand with his lips.

For many days he had realized that no words could be any comfort

to her. She was doomed, she thought - and damned. Von Hecklemetz

renewed the attack.

"Does this spirit,"he asked, "possess you now more

than half the time and make you have wicked thoughts and do

wicked things?"

"Soon", she said, "it will possess me all the time, and

then all my thoughts will be wicked all the time."

"When you have brought a dead man back," he asked,

"you feel an exceedingly wicked happiness?"

"Yes," she said.

"You and the black man, and new others whom he will

initiated, are in a conspiracy to surplant theliving with the

dead".

"Nothing else," she said, seems to us worth thinking

about." Her voice, calm enough but with the deep note of

anxiety broke on the word. She drew her hands from

Martin's and got to her feet. "Don't you see that I am damned,"

she said, "and when the spirit possesses me altogether I shan't

be fit to live." She turned to her lover. "If you love me,

she continued, "you would give me something that would kill me.

When I am no longer myself ever at all will you promist to do

that?". He looked into her face with sad eyes and shook his

head. xxx

"I have loved you so much," she said, "and we were

going to be so happy.Now this has happened. I have to take back

the promise that I gave you." Tears ran down her cheeks.
Doctor Martin caught her close to him and held her strongly.

"You can't take your promise back," he said, "I won't
let you. Somehow we are going to find a way to help you, to
save you."

~~She made no direct answer to this. She said~~, "Promise
that when the worst happens you will kill me!"

Von Hecklemetz came darting back from the further end
of the room.

"That would do no good," he said. He would send you
back to us. You would come back to this house yourself one of
the living dead. Those who had loved you would not have any
place for you. Your mother, perhaps, would die of horror."

Her voice broke pitiously, "Isn't there anything that
you can do?" she asked. Von Hecklemetz did not immediately
answer this question.

"When you were in the church," he said, "When you
stood ~~looking upward at the stained-glass window~~ with outstretched arms you had suddenly the feeling that you were being
nailed to the cross. You felt as if spikes were being roughly
driven through your hands and feet. The pain was frightful
but you thought that you were being allowed to atone for what
you had done and this thought made you infinitely glad."

"Mary," said Dr. Martin, "Can't you possibly give us
some clew as to where the black man keeps himself?"

Von Hecklebetz shook his finger emphatically at Martin,
"Suppose she could, what would you do?"

"I'd kill the beast with my bare hands," said the Doctor.

"Yes," said she.

The little man's eyes twinkled as if a sudden and important thought had come to him.

" Tell me", he said, "did you feel that this frightful pain was washing your sins away?"

"Yes,", she said.

He walked the length of the room. He seemed to be delighted with himself.

-54-

"At the moment," said Von Hecklemetz, "his evil spirit might happen to be in Mary. You kill him and it will stay in her forever and that is the exact opposite of what must happen."

Once more the girl asked pitiously, "Is there nothing that you can do? Is there no way?"

"Yes," said Von Hecklemetz, "There is a way."

Hope came into her eyes, "Don't tell him what it is," she said, "because when the spirit sends for me next time I might be forced to tell him."

"Do you trust me absolutely?" said the scientist.

"Absolutely," she said.

"And you, Doctor?" questioned Von Hecklemetz.

"Everything that you have told me," said Doctor Martin, has turned out to true. At first, your talk about the power of the Occult seemed childish to me. I was sure that the wounds in Mary's hands and feet were caused by some physical agency. So did the rest of us. And then before our very eyes the edges of the wounds drew together and the wounds healed until there were no longer any traces of them. You have made me believe that Science leaves off where the Occult begins. You asked if I trust you absolutely. I trust no man more. But when you said just now that there is one way to save Mary, something in the tone of your voice made me shudder. What are we going to do?"

"I will tell you later and privately," said Von Hecklemetz, "and you will have to give your consent and youwill have to give your help, because it is the only way.

"Promise that you will," said the girl. Doctor Martin did not immediately give the promise.

"My dear," said Von Hecklemetz, clicking his heels

together and bowing over Mary's hand which he kissed, "I have

some preparations to make. God night!"

When the lovers were alone, Mary once more urged

her lover to give his word that he would not oppose Von Heckle-

metz' proposal whatever it was.

"Please promise," she said, "to help him.

"Suppose his way means terrible danger to you."

"What danger", she said, could be greater than that

in which I am now standing? If you love me," she continued,"you

will ~~me p~~ help him "

She came then into his arms like a homing pigeon and

he held her close to his breast for a long time.

Night had fallen. Fog, thick and thin, filled the

London streets, drifted into rooms through open windows, drifted

into areaways and made a mystery of every light. Across the

street fromthe Suffolk's house, was a deep areaway from which

Doctor Martin and Von Hecklemetz kept an eye on the doorway of

the Suffolk house while Von Hecklemetz unfolded his plan to

save Mary and the reasoning upon which it was based.

"When Mary goes to the black man," he said, "his spirit

~~is in her.~~ will have possession of her body. He, himself, is lying down, somewhere, a thing apparently without

any life in it."

"What do we do? " asked Dr. Martin, "wait ~~until the~~

~~spirit leaves her and goes back into him?~~"

"It will not do that in our presence, unless we can

first find some way to drive it out of Mary. Then it will have

to go back. Then when the spirit is back in the black man

we must fill him ~~with~~ full of lead. When he is dead, his evil

Page 55   - insert X

"We shall ~~halt~~ _{slaughter}," said Von Hecklemetz, "and wait.
We shall wait until his spirit has left her and gone back
to him. Then, we shall ~~fill him full of lead~~. _{open fire upon his foul body,} When he is
dead his evil spirit ~~will die too, and Mary, I think, will~~ _{will be out of his control}
~~not have any memory of him or the wicked things which he~~
~~forced her to do.~~ But if, by chance, his spirit does not
leave her body, then we shall have to drive it from her body
and back into his. The STIGMATA, ~~for her against this power.~~ _{was a power against this} _{evil force.}
While the wounds remain in her hands and feet, it
could not possess her but ~~as~~ _{when} they healed ~~and faded until~~ _{and} all
traces of them were lost, ~~the spirit~~ _{His UNHoly spirit} succeeded in forcing
its way into a complete possession of her. Now she has
no longer the power to bring back upon herself these four
piteous wounds. We must do that for her. I have here four
real spikes and a ~~real~~ hammer."

          _{Dr. Martin}
"Good God, man," cried ~~Von Hecklemetz~~, ~~"What are you~~
~~planning to do?"~~

~~Von Hecklemetz answered, "We are going to crucify her!"~~

spirit will die too, and Mary, I think, will not have

any memory of him or of the wicked things which he has forced

her to do."

"How," asked Dr. Martin, "do we drive the spirit from her?"

Von Hecklemetz brandished an object tied in cloth

which looked as if it might contain some tools. "With these!"

he said.

"What is in that package? " asked the doctor.

"Do you remember what happened to Mary in the church?

Her hands and feet were transfixed by imaginary spikes driven

by an imaginary hammer." "Of course," said Doctor Martin. Von Hecklemetz

"Good God, man!" cried Doctor Martin, "What are you

planning to do?"

"I have here," said Von Hecklemetz, "four real spikes

and a real hammer. The power of the Occult can not stand/the against

Stigmata, against the four pitaous wounds. We are going to

crucify her!"

"Are you stark, staring mad?" asked the doctor.

"She won't suffer any more than she suffered in the

church, and she won't die," answered the doctor Von Hecklemetz.

"I will have nothing to do with anything so monstrous!"

said the doctor.

"You will have to give your consent and your help,"

said Von Hecklemetz, "The evil spirit will be in Mary. She will

put up a furious battle. I am not strong enough to manage the

thing alone. If you won't help me she is lost. She will

become the a creature in which there is no wish and no thought

that is not wicked. There is, but then, one way in which the woman

~~From a hidden place across the street, Dr. Martin and Lord Avon watched the front door of the Suffolk's house. At the back of the house was a small garden space surrounded by a high brick wall. This wall was pierced by one gate which gave upon an alley-way. But the gate had not been used for many years and the key had been mislaid. If, therefore, the evil spirit came to possess her and take her away, she could only leave her house by the front door. Patience of the man who loved her and of that famous occultist Lord Avon was at length rewarded.~~ The door of the Suffolk house opened and Maud Suffolk came out. Even across the street in the misty twilight it could be seen that the eyes were not hers. They were cruel wicked eyes.

The street in which the Suffolks lived was suburban. It was shaded by two rows of fine old Elms. At the nearest corner was a cab stand which at the moment afforded parking space for two taxi-cabs on the watch for fares. Toward these vultures of the night Maud Suffolk moved swiftly with purposeful steps. Martin and Lord Avon, making use of the tree trunks to shield themselves from discovery, followed her at what they conceived to be a safe distance.

Miss Suffolk commandeered the first cab she came to and drove off at a sharp pace. The gentlemen followed her in the remaining taxi.

She lead them a wild chase through one suburb after another. At times, because in places the fog was so heavy, they feared that they would lose her. These fears were groundless. ~~The vehicle containing Miss Suffolk pulled up in front of that three storied~~ abandoned, desolate, Georgian house with which the reader is familiar. ~~She alighted, paid her fare, and dismissed the taxicab.~~

Then she entered the unkempt grounds and walked swiftly to the ~~from here~~
house which she entered by the front door. When this had closed
behind her, the two anxious men hurried after her. The heavy house
door was not locked or bolted. They went in. The floors of the
house were thick with dust and it was easy to pick out the direction
in which she had gone. The marks of many feet or of a few feet,
going and coming many times, had made a distinct pathway diagonally
from the front door to a smaller door at the right side of the hall
under the stairhead. Otherwise the dust had not been disturbed for
years. The path through the dust lead them into the subterranes
of the house and indeed to the head of a certain ~~stoon~~ stone stair, the
treads of which had been worn hollow by generations of feet. As
they descended a few steps, a scene hitherto cut off by an arch which
might have been Roman, was gradually disclosed. At one side of a
narrow arched cellar there sat in a high-backed oak chair a man who
was obviously dead. He answered to Miss Suffolk's description of the
man with whom she had gone away from the dinner dance ~~after it eyes~~
~~of that man had become lifeless.~~ In his hand, which rested on the
arm of the chair, he held a tall altar candle. At the end of the
cellar, lying upon his back, his hands folded upon his breast, in
the dress of a gentleman's servant, lay a negro with snow white hair.
His eyes were ~~closed~~ dead and staring; he neither drew a breath nor moved a muscle.
Across from the dead man who sat in the chair, was an immense arched
door of heavy oak planks, bound together by ornamental irons. ~~Maud~~
~~Suffolk was standing~~ walked slowly towards ~~the prostrate negro~~ knelt down beside the ~~and looking down on his~~
~~feet.~~ body. The sound of steps descending the stair caused her to turn
and when she saw that those who descended the stair were Dr. Martin
and Lord Avon, she screamed, but not with fear. The scream told a

243

-57-

The door of the Suffålk house opened and Maud Suffolk
came out. Even across the street inthe misty twilight it could
be seen that the eyes were not hers. They were cruel wicket eyes.

The street in which the Suffolks lived was suburban.
It was shaded by two rows of fine old Elms. At the nearest
corner was a cab stand which at the moment afforded parking
space for two taxicabs on the watch for fares. Toward these
vultures of the night Maud Suffolk moved swiftly with purposeful
steps. Martin and ~~Lord Avon~~ Von Hecklemetz, making use of the tree trunks to
shield themselves from discovery, followed her at what they con
ceived to be a safe distance.

Miss Suffolk commandeered the first cab she came to
and dróve off at a sharp pace. The gentlemen followed her in the
remaining. taxi.

She lead them a wild chase through one suburb after
another. At times, because of places the fog was so heavy, they
feared that they would lose her.

These fears were groundless. The vehicle containing
Mary Suffolk came to a stop on the edge of a little wood. She
alighted, paid her fare and disappeared among the trees. Doctor
Martin and Von Hecklemetz followed her xx on foot as soon as it
seemed safe for them to do so. They followed her to a three-
story Georgian house standing in the midst of unkept grounds.
~~which the ragged~~ They saw her go up three broad shallow steps
and enter the house by the front door. Presently and very
cautionsly they followed.

The floors of the house were ~~were~~ thick with dust and
it was easy to pick out the direction in which she had gone.

The marks of ~~many feet or of a few~~ feet, going and coming many

times, had made a distinct pathway diagonally from the front

door to a smaller door at the right side of the hall under

the stairhead. Otherwise the dust had not been disturbed for

years. The path through the dust lead them into the subterranes

of the house and indeed to the head of a certain stone stair,

the treads of which had been worn hollow by generations of feet.

As they descended a few steps, a scene hitherto cut off by

an arch which might have been Roman, was gradually disclosed.

At one side of a narrow arched cellar there sat in a high-backed

oak chair a man who was obviously dead. He answered to Miss

Suffolk's description of the man with whom she had gone away

from the dinner dance. In his hand, which rested on the arms

of the chair, he held a tall altar candle. ~~At the end of the~~

~~cellar~~, *within the circle of light* lying upon his back, his hands folded upon his breast,

in the dress of a gentlemen's servant, lay a negro with ~~xxx~~

snow white hair. His eyes were dead and staring; he neither

drew a breath nor moved a muscle. Across from the dead man who

sat in the chair, was an immense arched door of heavy oak

planks, bound together by ornamental irons. ~~Mary walked~~

~~slowly towards and knelt down beside the body~~

Crouching on the stairway, looking over the solid

stone balister, Doctor Martin and Von Hecklemetz saw Mary

Suffolk walk slowly forward and kneel beside the body of the

prostrate negro. So, kneeling, she began to sway her body and

make those clinching and unclinching regent gestures with her

hands with which the reader is already familiar.

Doctor Martin, driven by hatred and without regard

to reason, leveled the automatic which he carried naked in

his hand, wrested the long ominous barrel on the top of the

balistrade and began to take a careful coldly calculated

aim at the negro.

"Wait - wait!," whispered Von Hecklemetz, "Wait till

the soul is entirely out of her body and has gone back into

his."

In withdrawing his weapon, a stone no longer bound to

its place by mortar was dislodged and fell with a startling

thud to the floor of the cellar. Mary Suffolk lept to her

feet and turned toward the sound. Her eyes, when she recog-

onized her lover and ~~the alchemist~~ blazed like a tiger's.

The two men hurried down the stair ~~and ran~~ toward her.

"Don't use that gun," ~~cried~~ Von Hecklemetz, "~~That~~

black soul is still in ~~the woman's~~ body."

While they were ~~running~~ toward her, a change had

come over ~~Miss~~ Suffolk~~'s~~ . The spirit of the witch doctor

which was in her and controlled her was not only an evil

spirit but a cunning, dexterous, quick-thinking spirit.

~~But whenever the spirit spoke through her mouth, it spoke~~

~~with its own voice and not with hers.~~ Her eyes were no

longer so burning bright. The scowl of hatred had been

smoothed from her forehead, ~~and although she spoke in the~~

voice of the witch doctor, truly and fearful and a wonderful

thing to have heard, she spoke. ~~pleadingly.~~

"Oh Arthur," she said, "Why couldn't you have waited

a few moments? His ~~awful~~ soul still possessed me and compelled

but it was in the very act of passing out of my body and

going back into his. Even now, though I speak in his voice,

he has only partial possession of me but if you harmed his

you love can be saved and restored to you, and you won't take it either for her sake or your own!"

"Is it the only way," cried Doctor Martin in his desperation.

"It is the only way," ~~said Doctor Douglas~~, and then with a finger to his lips, he said, "Ssh! Look!"

"For one who is so learned, it is incredible that you
should so have blundered."

Von Hecklemetz, with a twinkle in his eye, but
a twinkle full of malice, said, "Blundered! What makes
you think so?"

With her eyes becoming a little more defiant, she said,
"The one chance - the only chance you will ever have to
destroy me, you have thrown away."

"You forget," said Von Hecklemetz, "there is a power
far greater than that of evil, and with this power I will
drive your wicked soul into that vile vody lying there, and
then destroy it."

This did not alarm her. It seemed more to antagonize
her, and with a sneer of contempt, she said,

"Of the Occult, you have learned very little."

"But enough, to defeat you," cried Von Hecklemetz.

Unwrapping the package he carried with him, he
held aloft a hammer and four large iron spikes. At the sight
of these implements of torture, the spirit of the witch doctor
seemed to be burning its way through her eyes. It penetrated
the thick lenses of the eye-glasses worn by Professor Von
Hecklemetz. It seemed to be penetrating through
the spirit
eyes into his very soul. Slowly, he seemed to lean forward;
slowly, he took a half a step forward; his body swayed but he
fought against this unholy force. With difficulty, he raised
his hand. Fighting all the while against this evil power,
his hand reached his glasses and he removed them from his eyes.

A relief came over him. He relaxed as he stepped back, and said,

"Without my glasses, your eyes grow very dim. They lose their effect."

But the soul of the witch doctor was not ready to accept defeat. Once again, her eyes lost the burning light. Once again, the scowl of hatred was slowly leaving her face. She turned to Doctor Martin and with a voice that was softer, but still that of the witch doctor, she said,

"Arthur, though his spirit is within me and I am compelled to use his voice, I, Mary Suffolk, know what I am saying. There is a way - a way to release me from his control. If, when his soul reenters his body, - if you will allow him to leave here in peace, he will go back in where he came from, I will be free forever."

"I will promise, with all my soul," cried Doctor Martin.

Her eyes seemed to twinkle with pleasure. She reached out her hand towards him, and said,

"Then give me the revolver."

"Never," cried Von Hanklemetz, as he placed his glasses to his eyes again, "Never! I, too, know some of your thoughts - especially the one to get possession of that gun and kill us both.

She seemed to ignore the professor. Slowly she took a step forward towards Doctor Martin , and still pleading with the voice of the witch doctor, she said,

"Arthur, I have not the physical strength to fight you and get the revolver. Can't you understand that this it is only me whom he will trust?"

Professor Von Hecklemetz's shrewd eyes were watching every move she made; wqtching the Martin as he stood before him still hesitating to give in; watching as she took another step forward towards him. The voice, with its pleading tone continued,

"Is it not better this way than to subject me to the awful torture you have planned. I have gone through that torture, Arthur, please don't make me suffer it again."

As she placed her arms gently about his neck, her eyes began to blaze - blaze with a fire that penetrated into his. His intentions were to crush her to him - to hold her safely in his arms and never let her go, but these thoughts seemed to leave him. He stood there staring into her eyes. Then, slowly he removed one of her arms from around his neck and was placing the gun in her hand,but as quick as a rattlesnake strikes, Von Hecklemetz struck - and the gun flew from her hand across the floor. Seizing her by the arms

body now, his soul will reign in my body for ever and ever
and I will be as wicked as he."

She turned to Von Hecklemetz and the eyes which
the witch doctor's spirit had tried to make look kindly at
the younger man, seemed now to have in them a glint of
mischief and triumph.

"You," she said, "have had the only chance that youwill
ever have andyou have blundered."

Von Hecklemetz returned the look with a twinkling one
of his own but the twinkle was full of malice.

"Perhaps," he said."What makes you think so?"

"Because his soul is still within me and I know its
thoughts. It will not leave me until it is assured that when
it has returned into its own body t~~hey~~ will be allowed to
leave this place in safety."

"~~Let~~ that black devil ~~get out~~ of her life?" exclaimed
Martin.

"Never!" said Von Hecklemetz.

"Aethur!" she pleaded in the voice of the witch doctor,
"You loved me once. If you harm his empty body, the soul
that has left it and is in my body will stay in me forever
and you and I will be lost to each other forever."

Von Hecklemetz had been watching and listening with
the greatest intensity. He felt that his own sharp wits were
clashing with wits which might well be sharp.

"Promise," ~~xhex~~ he said, "that you will do nothing
rash."

"Very well," said Martin. "I promis."

"To him," said Mary Suffolk, "A promise is not enough. He doesn't trust either of you. He only trusts me. Give me the gun and promise that when his body comes to life and his soul is back in me, to let him go free. If you will do that, and I know all his thoughts, he will xx never molest me again." She reqched forward her hand asif expecting that the gun would be handed to her.

"Oh, no," said Von Hecklemetz, sharply, "I know some of your thoughts too. You would like to get hold of that gun and kill us both."

To this, she paid no heed. "Arthur," she said, "Don't you even love your memory of me? Perhaps my body is still beautiful to you. Take me in your arms. Hold me close. Promise to let him go and give me the gun."

She put her arms around him and looked a long time into his eyes.

Von Hecklemetz watched them both like a cat and it seemed to him as if the surgeon were losing control of his own will. His arms, which had clasped her, automatically loosened. He stepped back from her and a moment later, holding it by the barrel, he extended the automatic toward her hand, which reached forward to take it. Her fingers had begun to close upon the stock when Von Hecklemetz with an excited cry leapt forward, dashed the gun to the floor and seizing the girl by the arms tried to thrust her in the direction of the heavy oak door. Angered by what looked like an unprovoked xxxxit assault upon the woman he loved, Doctor Martin shouted,

"Have you gone mad?"

"No," shouted the little man, "You're the mad one,"
and still seeking to overpower her, he added, "A moment more
and we ~~would be dead~~ ^nothing would have been^."

These words had perhaps no significance for Doctor
Martin. He seized Von Hecklemetz roughly by the arm and ~~asked~~
shook him lose from the girl.

"Leave her alone," he said and glared angrily at him.
The little man glowered back. The girl stood motionless and
her eyes blazed. They were wholly evil and at the same time
deeply thoughtful and astute. Speaking more gently,
Doctor Martin said, "But didn't you hear her say that the
gun had to be in her possession?"

"You fool!" said Von Hecklemetz, "Did you think that
it was Mary's ^Soul that was talking?~~ ~~voice that said the gun must be in her possession?~~
Mary didn't say it. It was said to us by that ~~cunning, wicked,~~ ^cunning,^
unholy spirit which possesses her and which seeks her destruction"

There came from Mary's throat a scream of rage like
nothing earthly. It was the cry of an animal, a jungle
cry. Her eyes on fire, she made a dash for the gun. But
Von Hecklemetz was too quick for her. Again he grappled with
her and now, brought to his senses by that terrible cry,
Doctor Martin came to his aid.

(top of page 59 to "A")

then

("A") Meanwhile a change had come over the ~~press~~ prostrate
negro as Miss Suffolk's screams and struggles became less.
Light appeared in his dead eyes. They began to twinkle

story of implacable hatred and defiance.

They pushed her to her and tried to pinion her arms, but she fought
them like a wild cat, biting and scratching. By the time that they
had dragged her to the oak door and pressed her against it, both men
were bleeding. Dr. Martin was a powerful man and had uncommon skill
with his hands, but it was all that he could do with the help of
the prof to hold her with her back to the door, her right arm doubled,
so that she could not use it, and her left arm extending from her body
at a right angle, the palm of the hand outward. She still screamed
and struggled with the utmost fury of energy. Martin was handicapped
by the fact that he could not look at the awful eyes which blazed
in her head. She no longer seemed to resemble the woman he loved,
even physically. But when the little man cried, "Spike her to the door,"
he could not and it was Heck Helmetz, wielding his hammer with a
vim and accuracy, which was surprising in so small and old a man,
nailed first her left hand to the door, and then he
her right. He now knelt to drive the spikes
through her feet. Suddenly he became aware that the Mary Suffolk's screaming
and the struggling had stopped altogether. He looked upward. Maud Suffolk's
head had fallen forward and sideways on her breast. If her hands had
not been spiked to the door, she would have fallen to the ground. Her
face had at once a look of great suffering and peace. She seemed
symbolic of a holy thing.

But to that quick thinker, Heck Helmetz, the symbol told a different
story.

"Quick man quick!" he cried, "Shoot him down!"
Half way towards the gun and where he
A little way from the wall against which it had been lying,
the witch doctor crouched and looked with horribly concentrated
tigerish eyes into the faces of the two men. possessing it
...of the pistol and Martin reached it first
attempt to of that place unobserved. He had been

Martin gets Gun

He was

careful not to cast a glance at the bleeding symbol which had
Unholy
driven his ~~wicked troubled~~ spirit from the body of the beautiful
girl and back into his own. From his crouching position he sprang
suddenly ~~straight at the throat of the tall man~~ with the heavy,
for
~~But Martin was the first to reach it and~~
automatic. ~~But in mid-air a flash blinded him and the force of~~
the heavy bullet traveling at high velocity checked ~~his~~ this spring
of the witch Doctor and
~~and~~ brought him crumpled and writhing ~~and screaming~~ to the floor.
In the automatic there remained eight cartridges. One after the
other with a perfect fury of speed and hatred, Dr. Martin emptied
these into the body of the screaming, writhing negro. The last
shot delivered at close quarters drilled a hole half an inch in
his
diameter into the right temple, ~~and blew off the other side of his~~
~~head.~~ The witch doctor lay still in death.
~~During all of this operation, Maid Suffolk had fainted.~~ It
was while she was in this condition that they succeeded in wrenching
the spikes loose from the door and withdrawing them from the
wounded hands. Dr. Martin had brought the necessary dressings.
While he dressed her wounds she came to and gave him a brave smile.
He picked her up in his arms and moved toward the foot of the stair.
did
It ~~would~~ not seem as if a man so strong could be also so pitying
and so gentle. He made little murmuring sounds over her that reminded one of a dove cooing. His attention, as well as that of
Lord Avon ~~Lord Avon~~ Dr Martin, was suddenly directed to the dead man who had been
sitting in the high backed chair. It was the sound of the altar
to   and
candle falling on the floor where it still burned, sputtered ~~which~~
had for a moment distracted them from their solicitude to the
wounded girl. As they looked, the dead man collapsed in the chair
until he sprawled out ~~sideways over one of the arms~~
putting out the candle
"He is no longer a dead man who had come back, Said Lord Avon.
"He is nothing but a dead man. What has happened to him at this

-63-

and snap. His wicked soul, driven from her body by the

symbolism of the crucifiction, it was returning as swiftly as it

could to his. Presently, his eyes blazed just as hers had

blazed. He got to his knees and stealthily began to creep toward

the automatic pistol which lay on the floor.

>   (back to rest of page 59,
>   at "Suddenly" just after
>   the "A")
>
>   Finish page, then down from
>   top of page 60 as far as "A")

("A")   The dead man who sat in the tall chair and held the

candle began slowly to collapse forward. The candle fell

from his hand. The dead man fell forward now out of his

chair, crashing heavily down upon the candle and putting it

out. There was darkness in which could be heard the cool,

measured voice of Von Hecklemetz,

>   "SO IT WILL BE WITH ALL THE OTHERS, DEATH HAS
>   RECLAIMED ITS OWN."

>   (copy page 61 from "Maud Suffolk, her
>   mind at peace, etc" to end of page)

END

very moment is happening to all those other dead man who have been coming back during these frightful days, driving those who had loved them from their homes in stark terror and making the beginning of crowding out the living from the earth. The power which could bring them back, motivate them and move them here and there like passes on a chess-board, no longer exists.

Maud Suffolk, her mind at peace, her loving troth with Martin replighted, soon recovered from her wounds. But the spikes which had been laced into her of small diameter and these scars would be no more than so many little spots of silver. During her convalescence she liked to lounge in a deep chair and stroke the head of her beloved who knelt beside her.

Whenever the little river boat came up from Wamba with the mail, Trelawney made an effort through that medium to keep up with the times. He attended to his correspondence and read all the newspapers religiously. But Suffolk, a ghastly shadow of himself with haunted eyes, neither opened his letters nor glanced at the news. Trelawney sometimes feared that his youthful companion would end by going mad. An item in the London Times dated more than two months ago caught his eye. He read it through swiftly and a look of relief and happiness came into his eyes.

"Cheerio old top," he cried, "Here's news for you. You'll not be all alone and by yourself again."

"Have they got him?" Asked Suffolk with sudden.

"They have got them both," said Trelawney, "Both Boris and that damned witch doctor and they have both been burned to ashes. All the dead who walked the streets of London and desolated English homes are in their graves again. The dead will not come back anymore because there is no longer any power that can make them. The horror is over."

THE END

Author Biographies

Nathaniel Bell teaches film history at Biola University. A graduate of Chapman University's Dodge College of Film and Media Arts, his master's thesis on Curtis Harrington won the Cecil Award for outstanding film scholarship. His criticism has appeared in the *Los Angeles Daily News*, *Los Angeles Review of Books* and *LA Weekly*, where he currently covers new releases. He lives in Whittier with his wife Emily, their three sons, and a German Shepherd.

Robert Guffey is a lecturer in the Department of English at California State University–Long Beach. His books include *Widow of the Amputation and Other Weird Crimes* (Eraserhead Press, 2021), *Bela Lugosi's Dead* (Crossroad Press, 2021), *Until the Last Dog Dies* (Night Shade/Skyhorse, 2017), *Chameleo: A Strange but True Story of Invisible Spies* (OR Books, 2015), *Heroin Addiction, and Homeland Security* (OR Books, 2015), *Spies & Saucers* (PS Publishing, 2014), and *Cryptoscatology: Conspiracy Theory as Art Form* (TrineDay, 2012). He also collaborated with Gary D. Rhodes on the non-fiction book *Bela Lugosi and the Monogram Nine* (BearManor Media, 2019). Forthcoming from Planet Bizarro Press is Guffey's third novel, *Dead Monkey Rum*.

Will Dodson, Ph.D., teaches courses on rhetoric, film and literature at UNC Greensboro. His essays on Tod Browning, Jess Franco, Hugo Haas, Shirley Jackson and various film genres have appeared in edited collections and journals including *Quarterly Review of Film & Video* and *Film International*. With David A. Cook, he is co-editor of *The Anthem Series on Exploitation and Industry in Global Cinema*, a book series on exploitation films and filmmakers and the various ways in which they have subsidized mainstream cinema and culture. He and Kristopher Woofter co-edit *American Twilight: The Cinema of Tobe Hooper* (University of Texas Press, 2021).

Jan Alan Henderson has published for over three decades in such periodicals as *American Cinematographer*, *Filmfax* and *Cult Movies*. His book titles include *Speeding Bullet: The Life and Bizarre Death of George Reeves* (M. Bifulco, 1999), *Behind the Crimson Cape: The Cinema of George Reeves* (M. Bifulco, 2005), *The Legendary Lydecker Brothers* (CreateSpace, 2010) and *Rocky Jones, Space Ranger* (CreateSpace, 2013). His fiction titles include *Crypt 39* (CreateSpace, 2016) and *Whispers from the Canyons of Mountain Laurel* (Independent, 2020).

Gary D. Rhodes, Ph.D., currently serves as Full Professor of Media Production at Oklahoma Baptist University. He is the author of *The Perils of Moviegoing in America* (Bloomsbury, 2012), *Tod Browning's Dracula* (Tomahawk, 2015) and *The Birth of the American Horror Film* (Edinburgh, 2018), as well as seven books on Bela Lugosi. He is a founding editor of *Horror Studies: An Interdisciplinary Journal*, and he serves as co-editor of the ReFocus series at Edinburgh University Press. Rhodes is also the writer-director of the documentary films *Lugosi: Hollywood's Dracula* (1997) and *Banned in Oklahoma* (2004). His forthcoming book is entitled *Vampires in Silent Cinema*.

Acknowledgments

I would like to express gratitude to the various archives, libraries and museums that kindly assisted during the research phase of this project: the Billy Rose Theater Division of the New York Public Library, the Harry Ransom Center at the University of Texas at Austin, the Library of Congress in Washington, D. C., the Los Angeles Public Library, and the Media History Digital Library. The Tod Browning scripts housed at the Margaret Herrick Library of the Academy of Motion Picture Arts and Sciences were invaluable to this project.

I also wish to offer thanks to a number of individuals who gave so much of their time and support that they proved crucial to this project's completion: the late Forrest J Ackerman, Matthew E. Banks, Buddy Barnett, Stephen R. Bissette, Michael F. Blake, Kevin Brownlow, Mario Chacon, Bill Chase, Ned Comstock, Michael Copner, Robert Cremer, Richard Daub, Kristin Dewey, Jack Dowler, the late William K. Everson, the late Phillip Fortune, Beau Foutz, Donald F. Glut, Bill Kaffenberger, Roy Kinnard, Robert J. Kiss, Leonard J. Kohl, the late Mark A. Miller, Ben Ohmart, Donald Rhodes, Phyllis Rhodes, William Rosar, Robert L. Singer, Anthony Slide, Carter Smith, John Soister, David Stenn, Laura Wagner, David Wentink and Glenn P. White.

I would particularly like to thank John Antosiewicz for providing so many invaluable film stills, and to Russell McGee for sharing his own original copy of the script of *The Revolt of the Dead*. I am deeply grateful to George Chastain for creating such a tremendous faux-movie poster for *The Revolt of the Dead*. Special thanks to contributing authors Nathaniel Bell, Will Dodson, Jan Alan Henderson and Robert Guffey. And of course I am appreciative of editor Tom Weaver, for including this volume in his "Scripts from the Crypt" series.

Gary D. Rhodes
2022

Endnotes

1 Coincidentally, *Something Wicked This Way Comes* was published in 1962, the year Tod Browning died.

2 Foma is a word coined by Kurt Vonnegut in his 1963 novel *Cat's Cradle*. It means "harmless untruths."

3 Gilbert starred in Browning's 1927 silent *The Show* as Cock Robin, a womanizing scamp. *Fast Workers* had Gilbert playing Gunner Smith, a similarly dubious character.

4 Though Browning had no writing credit on *Miracles for Sale*, the film's narrative of a former magician (Young) who makes his living debunking phony psychics and mediums fits neatly into Browning's common themes.

5 Sam Moskovitz, *A. Merritt: Reflections in the Moon Pool* (Philadelphia: Oswald Train, 1985), 121-22.

6 The ritual involved gutting a live lamb so that its blood flowed over the child's naked body. Merritt describes the child as anemic prior to the ritual; three months later, he visited the farm again to find her healthy. Merritt made the somewhat dubious conclusion that the ritual must have worked! See Moskovitz, pp. 367-69.

7 Merritt's original title was *The Dolls of Mme. Mandilip*, but *Argosy* asked for something more dramatic.

8 In the novel, Madame Mandilip is of indeterminate origin, but it's vaguely implied that she's Eastern European or Slavic. In "The Wondersmith," the toymaker is male and Romani.

9 Browning grew up in the Jim Crow South, and like most carnival players and vaudevillians performed on occasion in blackface. He got his start working as one of D.W. Griffith's troupe, and is rumored to have played a robed Klansman in *The Birth of a Nation* (1915). None of these facts tell us Browning's own views on race, but neither do they suggest he was progressive in that regard.

10 The sequence bears a striking if coincidental resemblance to the famous "Baptism murders" sequence in *The Godfather* (1972), which cross-cuts from Michael Corleone attending his infant son's baptism and his henchmen murdering his Mafia rivals.

11 See Richard Koszarski, *The Man You Loved to Hate: Erich von Stroheim and Hollywood* (New York: Oxford University Press, 1983), 278. Koszarski asserts that "directors like Tod Browning, Clarence Brown, and George Fitzmaurice, all of whom knew [von Stroheim] from better days," would request him for story conferences and collaborations, where he specialized in "adult bits of business" (275). That may or may not be the case with *The Devil-Doll*.

12 See Bret Wood, "The Witch, the Devil, and the Code: A Horror Story of Hollywood in the Golden Age," *Film Comment*, vol. 28, #6 (November-December 1992), 54-55.

13 Alexander Payne's 2017 film *Downsizing*, starring Matt Damon, may have been inspired by *The Devil-Doll's* first act. In it, Norwegian scientists perfect a shrinking process in order to reverse the effects of climate change by reducing humanity's impact on the environment.

14 This is the scene that disturbed Breen so: "Toto and Lorraine in the living room by the fireplace, little Toto standing beside him holding up the back flap of his nightgown. Then as Lorraine looks down at the kid, she begins to laugh. THE CAMERA PANS around so as to show the infant Toto's little bare behind warming itself at the fire."

15 Surprisingly, the detail of Lavond's wife's suicide was included in the final film and got past the censor.

16 Quoted by Vivian Sobchack from an interview in which Westover is credited as "Mrs. William S. Hart Sr." Westover was married to Hart (a close friend of Browning's) from 1920 until 1927. See Bernd Herzogenrath, editor, *The Films of Tod Browning* (London: Black Dog, 2006), 33.

17 Reynold Humphries explored the insidious depiction of capitalism in *The Devil-Doll*, and helpfully pointed out that "Radin" is French for "miserly." See Humphries, *The Hollywood Horror Film 1931-1941: Madness in a Social Landscape* (Lanham MD: Scarecrow, 2006), 199-202.

Made in the USA
Middletown, DE
08 November 2023

42210347R00150